"He's really taken his game to the next level and that's why he's one of the top bowlers in world cricket."
– Virat Kohli speaking to reporters about Mitchell Starc ahead of a Test match in February 2017

First published in Great Britain 2024 by Red Shed, part of Farshore

An imprint of HarperCollins*Publishers*
1 London Bridge Street, London SE1 9GF
www.farshore.co.uk

HarperCollins*Publishers*
Macken House, 39/40 Mayor Street Upper,
Dublin 1, D01 C9W8

Red Shed is a registered trademark of HarperCollins*Publishers* Ltd.

Copyright © HarperCollins*Publishers* Limited 2024

Cover illustration by Carl Pearce.

ISBN 978 0 00 860890 3
Printed and bound in the UK using 100% Renewable Electricity at CPI Group (UK) Ltd.
001

A CIP catalogue record for this title is available from the British Library.

Stay safe online. Any website addresses listed in this book are correct at the time of going to print.
However, Farshore is not responsible for content hosted by third parties. Please be aware that online
content can be subject to change and websites can contain content that is unsuitable for children.
We advise that all children are supervised when using the internet.

Some conversations in this book have been fictionalised, however these are based on
real life events using sources from the public domain including video and newspaper
interviews, video footage and written accounts. Every effort has been made to
avoid misrepresenting the events portrayed in this book.

This book contains FSC™ certified paper and other controlled
sources to ensure responsible forest management.

For more information visit: www.harpercollins.co.uk/green

MITCHELL STARC

Written by Clive Gifford

RED■
SHED

★ CHAPTER 1 ★

Fast and Furious

Sunday, 15 November 2015.

"Say, this is one dangerous man!" exclaimed cricket commentator Mark Nicholas, as Mitchell Aaron Starc took yet another wicket for Australia.

Mitchell was playing for Australia on day three of the second Trans-Tasman Test against New Zealand at the WACA (Western Australian Cricket Association) ground in Perth. Fast, bouncy and often rock-hard, the pitches at the WACA have a fearsome reputation for being deadly for batters. So too, did Mitch!

Although he was only 25 years old and still relatively new to international cricket, Mitch had already taken over 200 wickets for Australia in Tests, One Day Internationals (ODIs) and Twenty20 (T20) games. He was an exciting left-arm fast bowler, sometimes a little wayward, often quick and hostile, and always watchable. He was famous for his yorker – a ball aimed to pitch full (near the batter's feet) and hit the stumps or pads, to get batters out leg before wicket (LBW).

Australia had scored 559. Mitch had contributed precisely zero to the score. Normally, a good lower order batter, he'd been outfoxed by spinner Mark Craig and hit the ball straight up into the air to be caught easily. Craig took three wickets in that over, but couldn't stem the Aussie tide of runs.

In the previous Test match, Mark Craig had frustrated Mitch . . . a lot. Craig and Trent Boult

were the last pair of New Zealand batters and
Australia expected to get them out quickly
to win the game. But the pair stuck around
for 49 balls, scoring 46 runs.

After Craig had hit him for three fours,
Mitch reacted. He retrieved the ball, spun
and threw a wild throw in the batter's general
direction. It missed Craig and raced away to
the boundary, giving New Zealand four runs
for free. Australia eventually won, but Mitch
was given a serious telling off by match
referee Roshan Mahanama and fined half
of his match fee for his actions.

Off the pitch, Mitch Starc was polite, modest
and made good friends with cricketers in other
teams. But something clicked as soon as he
walked onto a cricket ground, and he became
extremely competitive. Earlier that year, he'd
been given a warning for yelling in the face of

Indian batter Murali Vijay after bowling him out.

In this second Test, New Zealand were motoring at 332 for two. Despite having already bowled 16 overs, Australia needed another fiery spell from Mitch.

Speed guns in the stadium measured the pace of balls bowled. Mitch began his new spell bowling just above 140 kilometres per hour – reasonably rapid – and he troubled both batters with his pace and swing.

A gentle wind – known as the Freemantle Doctor – blew in off the nearby Swan river as Mitch strode back to his bowling mark and turned to run in.

"C'mon, Mitch – crank it up!" yelled a teammate in encouragement. Mitch obliged. By his fourth over, he was bowling rockets!

Most of his deliveries were over 150 kilometres per hour – that's fast and gives batters so little time to react.

Mitch's first delivery to Brendon McCullum caught his bat and flew over the slips. The second, even faster, also clipped Brendon's bat and whizzed towards Mitch's teammate Nathan Lyon, fielding at second slip. Such was its speed, Nathan couldn't get his hands into position in time and the chance was dropped.

Mitch was annoyed, but tried not to show it to his teammates. Instead, he channelled his fury into bounding in even quicker. The last ball of the over zoomed towards McCullum at almost 155 kilometres per hour. It crashed into McCullum's bat and a chunk of wood exploded away. Mitch had broken Brendon McCullum's bat! A replacement had to be brought out.

The crowd were loving this.

"One hundred and fifty-five kilometres per hour? That's super quick!"

"My car doesn't go that fast!"

"C'mon, faster. FASTER!"

Mitch began the gruelling 21st over of the innings. His cricket trousers were covered in brown dirt from diving when fielding, and red marks where he'd been shining the ball. He had bowled around 400 high-speed overs in the previous six months. It was a testing workload on his slim 1.96 metre-tall frame. Yet still he kept bowling at over 150 kilometres per hour.

In the fourth ball of the over, he unleashed an absolute thunderbolt of a yorker. The ball was sizzlingly fast and gun-barrel straight. Ross Taylor was surprised by its sharpness and just got enough of his bat down to stop it smashing his stumps.

"Best yorker in world cricket, right there," gushed the commentator on TV.

Then his colleague spotted the speed gun and chipped in. "That's 160.4 kilometres per hour, that one . . ."

"C'mon, Mitch!"

"He's got some rhythm, hasn't he? You can see him snapping through his action."

The WACA crowd revved up when they saw the speed displayed. Mitch had just broken one of the longest-standing records in Test cricket. His 160.4 kilometres per hour delivery was the fastest ever bowled in Test cricket. Mitch had just broken West Indian legend Andy Roberts' record from 1975.

The crowd were on their feet and clapping as Mitch bounded in to bowl the next ball. Bowling smart, he released a slightly slower delivery (149 kilometres per hour), which caught the edge of Ross Taylor's bat and flew away.

"Catch it!" yelled one of Mitch's teammates.

All-rounder Mitchell Marsh, fielding at gully (behind and to the right of the batter), threw himself at the ball, but couldn't hold on. Then, a second Aussie fielder dived, but couldn't stop the ball slamming into the boundary. Four! Starc trudged back to his mark. That's what it's like being a fast bowler at times – you create chances, but they're not taken.

Ross Taylor survived the Starc storm and went on to score a career-best 290 – still the highest Test innings by a batter visiting Australia. Mitch ended up with four wickets but bowled 37 lung-busting overs in the first innings alone. All that pace, all that effort and the game ended in a draw – that can be Test cricket sometimes.

After the game, Mitch chatted and joked with Ross Taylor and Brendon McCullum, who admitted it was one of the fastest spells they'd ever faced. But with Australia still 1–0 up in the series, the New Zealand batting coach, Craig McMillan, tried to play down Mitch's record-breaking delivery. He joked that speed guns weren't that reliable or accurate.

As cricketing website ESPNcricinfo reported in November 2015, McMillan had said, "I don't know, maybe someone in the truck was having a bit of fun [. . .] I'm not sure if maybe the wrong button was pushed."

Mitch, in return, invited the New Zealand coach to measure the speed of his bowling up close. "I'm happy for him to face me in the nets tomorrow, if he wants," Mitch said, smiling menacingly.

By then, Mitch was already focusing on the next Test. That's what top cricketers have to do. However they perform as an individual, they know they only succeed or fail together as a team.

As for bowling at express speed, Mitch

said afterwards, in a February 2016 interview with *Inside Cricket*. "There's times when it seems easy. It mightn't even feel fast, but everything's working nicely. That's when it comes out quickest."

⭐ CHAPTER 2 ⭐

Hard Yakka

Being a fast bowler is no picnic. It's not all terrifying batters with vicious bouncers, celebrating as wickets fall and raising your arms to the cheering crowd who are chanting your name!

Behind any fast bowler's best days on the pitch are weeks, months and years of toil and hard graft. An Australian slang term for this sort of gruelling work is 'hard yakka', from the Yagara Aboriginal language. So it was with Mitch's rise as a top pace bowler for Australia.

Thousands of hours are put into training and workouts in the gym to build strength, flexibility and fitness. That's just the start. Bowlers practise their ball grip and release, which must be spot-on to send the ball accurately to its target.

They also look to perfect their run-up towards the wicket. Pace bowlers work with coaches to make their approach as smooth, balanced and energy efficient as possible. They want to transfer as much of the speed and power of their run-up into the delivery, to send the ball zooming down the pitch under control.

Fast bowlers like Mitch sprint a 42.2 kilometre-long marathon in their run-ups every 2,000 balls or so they bowl. Mitch has bowled over 25,000 balls in first-class cricket, and for each ball bowled in a match, there'll be many more bowled in the nets during training and practice. Exhausting!

Then there's the most complicated part of all – the bowling action. This is where the player leaps, twists in the air, lands, then whips their bowling arm overhead with pace and power. This action really tests and stresses their body. As Pakistan pace bowling legend Shoaib Akhtar said in an interview with the *Cricket Monthly* in April 2015, "You have to be a bit abnormal to be a fast bowler [. . .] Pivoting and twisting your body when running in at full sprint is not normal."

The impact on the front foot as the bowler lands, for example, is equal to around seven times their body weight. Add in all the sprinting around to field the ball, plus running between the wickets when batting, and it is no wonder that bowlers complain of sore feet, legs and ankles!

Fast bowlers often get injuries. Mitch, for example, suffered a stress fracture in his lower back in September 2013. It resulted in him missing more than three months of cricket.

He has also missed games due to muscle problems in his left knee, right calf and, a few weeks before the 2015 World Cup, a groin strain. He had the exact same groin problem eight years later, shortly before the start of the 2023 World Cup. Scary! But one of the worst injuries Mitch has suffered occurred not during a match, but whilst training with Australia.

In the middle of fielding practice in September 2016, Mitch launched himself to take a catch, even though several of his teammates shouted, "Don't go for it!"

Mitch got his hands to the ball, but his left shin collided with a stump pushed into the ground. It ripped his trousers and gouged a deep, long cut up his left leg.

As Cricket Australia reported online in September 2016, Mitch's teammate Steve Smith said, "It was actually probably one of the most gruesome things I have ever seen."

Mitch was rushed to St George Hospital in

Sydney. There was lots of blood, but, fortunately, he hadn't broken any bones. He did need 30 stitches though to sew the cut up and had to walk around in a leg brace for weeks to let the injury heal.

This wasn't Mitch's only injury – he got another in the game after his 160 kilometres per hour ball. It was staged in Adelaide and was the world's first day/night Test match. Play began in the afternoon and continued late into the evening using floodlights and a bright pink (instead of red) ball for better visibility.

Australia were bowling on the first day and Mitch was on fire, having delivered nine overs of red-hot pace bowling.

Out!

New Zealand's young batter Kane Williamson was beaten by a trademark yorker from Mitch. He was out LBW (leg before wicket).

Out!

Mitch got New Zealand captain Brendon McCullum with a short, fast ball that was edged to the wicketkeeper. New Zealand were in real trouble at 98 for 5.

Out!

The stumps scattered as Mitch bowled Mitchell Santner with a delivery that angled in. New Zealand lost their sixth wicket.

Mitch's bowling figures were fabulous – nine overs, three wickets for just 24 runs, but he was in agony. He'd suffered a nasty stress fracture in his right foot as it landed whilst bowling. He was already carrying injuries to his right ankle, which meant having painkilling injections and surgery.

This injury occurred on the very first day of a five-day Test, so Australia would have to play with one player short for the rest of the match. Mitch couldn't bowl or field, and turned up to team training and preparation the next day on crutches and wearing a big, foam boot to protect his injured ankle.

Mitch watched as Australia struggled when batting. When his side lost their ninth wicket, they were still behind New Zealand's total. Mitch bravely went out to bat. Knowing he couldn't run between the wickets due to the broken bone, he swung his bat . . . and swung it hard.

He scored 24 in just 11 balls, striking two towering sixes and three thumping fours. Wow!

That should have been that. Mitch was seriously injured, but he was called into action one more time. Australia were within two runs of winning the match in the second innings when they lost another wicket. Out he hobbled to the middle to join fellow fast bowler, Peter Siddle. After a few tense balls were defended, Siddle drove the ball through the covers. Mitch had to hop up and down the wicket on one foot to complete the two runs needed for the win.

Mitch celebrated, but wouldn't play again for 189 days. It was a horrid time for this elite cricketer, with operations on his damaged ankle followed by endless rehabilitation, training and lots of work with physiotherapists. Mitch regretted missing not only Test matches, but also the T20i World Cup and the Indian Premier League (IPL).

But he recovered to win series and trophies again and be feared as one of the planet's most powerful fast bowlers. How did he bounce back from such big setbacks? What gave him the drive to play for his country for 15 years? Well, it all began in a suburb of Australia's largest city . . .

CHAPTER 3

Sunny Days in the Suburbs

"I'm going to play cricket for Australia, Mum."

"That's great, dear. Now, wash your hands before lunch."

Mitchell Aaron Starc was just five years old when he uttered those words, reported by the *Sydney Morning Herald* in January 2012. Born in 1990, his parents, Julie and Paul, had photos of him holding a little plastic cricket bat in his hand when he was just two and could barely walk. Mitch was the eldest of four children: a younger brother called Brandon and two sisters, Amanda and Taylah.

Amazing Cricket Stars – Mitchell Starc

All four spent lots of their leisure time outside. New South Wales has a warm climate with lots of sunny days – just perfect for roaming about and playing sport. The Starcs grew up in the Western Suburbs; some 25 kilometres to the east was the centre of Australia's biggest city, Sydney. There were plenty of open spaces and sports facilities for budding young sports stars where they lived. And it wasn't long before the close-by Olympic Stadium at Homebush was completed in time for the 2000 Summer Olympics.

Much of Mitch's early cricket was played in the garden of his family home. "Games pretty much finished when you hit the back window," recalled Mitch in a video interview with Cricket Australia in June 2019. "Game over and Mum would be chasing you down the street!"

The Starc family lived in a cul-de-sac, which meant no cars would come racing through.

Sunny Days in the Suburbs

This made it perfect as an arena for any sport the children wanted to play. Sometimes, a soccer ball would be kicked. Other times, an Aussie Rules football would be thrown around – this Australian 18-a-side team sport is played on large oval pitches with an oval ball, similar to a rugby ball.

"Caught it!"

"You dropped it!"

"No, I didn't."

Mitch would later become a big fan of Aussie Rules team, the Greater Western Suburbs Giants, and can often be found at games wearing a replica shirt. As a kid though, the most common game saw a tennis ball and cricket bat produced, with milk crates used as stumps.

If they weren't playing cricket in the cul-de-sac, the kids would head to the nearby car park in front of a warehouse to play . . .

until Mitch heard the tell-tale whistle from his father standing at the doorstep.

"Come inside. Dinner's ready."

Mitch's father, Paul, was an engineer and a big sports fan. He taught Mitch and the others the basics of how to play cricket. He would also sometimes carry his ladder over to the warehouse to climb wearily onto its roof. The reason? To retrieve all the lost tennis balls hit up there by Mitch and the other children.

Paul Starc's parents had emigrated to Australia from Czechoslovakia (which has since split into two countries: Slovakia and Czechia). He had played baseball for New South Wales as a youngster, but had become a cricket fan as he grew older. He volunteered to help run local youth cricket teams and clubs in his spare time. Mitch began playing club cricket at Berala Sports where his dad was, for a time, a coach for the Under-10s and club secretary.

Mitch's grandparents on his mum's side, Betty and Frank, owned a farm called Fairlight in northern New South Wales. Mitch used to enjoy visits there. He'd always have a bat and ball with him, and badger his grandad as soon as he saw him. In an interview with 9 News Australia in July 2019, Betty and Frank recalled how Mitchell used to call out, "Pop, pop, bowl us a ball." When Frank bowled the ball gently underarm, Mitch would protest, "No, no, not that way!"

One day after school, Mitch was picked up by his dad and taken on a great road trip to Canberra to see Steve Waugh play in a Prime Minister's XI match. Waugh was a highly successful captain of Australia who played 168 Tests, and was Mitch's first cricket idol.

"I think he got out for not many," recalled Mitch years later in a video interview with Cricket Australia in December 2019. "Steve then picked up a plastic chair and came down to one of the boundaries. There were just mountains of people and he signed autographs for hours. He's always been a hero of mine."

Whilst playing for Berala Sports, in competitions organised by Northern District Junior Cricket, Mitch began keeping wicket. He added a new hero to his list – the Australian wicketkeeper-batter, Adam Gilchrist. 'Gilly' had transformed the role of wicketkeeper in Test cricket by scoring quick runs with audacious attacking strokes.

"I just loved the way he saw the ball and tried to smack it," Mitch told Cricket Australia's online site in December 2019. "I still try and do that now!"

Gilchrist had replaced legendary keeper

Ian Healy in the Australian Test team in 1999. By a strange coincidence, around the same time, Ian Healy's niece played for one of the teams nine-year-old Mitch faced.

Alyssa Healy was the only girl in the Carlingford Waratah's Under-10s boys' team. She'd wanted to be a fast bowler but, like Mitch, also kept wicket and batted for her side. When both Mitch and Alyssa were picked to play for the Northern District representative team, which played matches each Sunday, they had to share wicketkeeping duties for four years. The pair stayed in touch as friends long after they'd left local youth cricket.

As Mitch grew into his teens, he played a lot of cricket, but he didn't give up on another sport he liked – soccer (called football in the UK). He played regularly for Lidcombe Churches Soccer Club, taking part in more than

200 matches and scoring 68 goals. His younger brother Brandon was a better player and would captain the side. Brandon also eclipsed Mitch in another sport: athletics.

Mitch had enjoyed athletics at school. He could run well and wasn't bad at the high jump either. But Mitch's high jumping wasn't a patch on his younger brother's. Brandon became an international high jumper representing Australia in international competitions such as the World Championships and the Olympics.

At the 2018 Commonwealth Games, Brandon's leap of 2.32 metres was enough to see him win the gold medal. His older brother cheered him on from the stands of the Carrara Stadium, then proudly took to social media to exclaim, "Get in there, boy! Awesome! Super proud, young fella."

⭐ CHAPTER 4 ⭐

Becoming a Bowler

Mitch's first real cricketing setback came when he was 12 years old. With good performances for his Northern District side and school teams, he'd hoped to get a call up to the state junior side – the New South Wales Emerging Blues.

A letter came but it told him he hadn't been selected. It was a bitter blow. Instead of crumpling it up and throwing it away, Mitch pinned it to his bedroom noticeboard. It would act as motivation during his teenage years. Obstacles have to be overcome; they were not going to stop him.

By the time he was 14, Mitch was enjoying playing as a wicketkeeper who could swing the bat hard and score some crucial runs lower down the batting order.

He decided to try out for the Under-16s side of 'Wests' – the Western Suburbs cricket club. The Under-16s played in the 'Greenies' – the Green Shield competition for the best young cricketers in the region. As a group of hopeful young players practised their fielding, the head coach, Neil D'Costa was startled. He'd just noticed one tall, spindly teenager running hard then throwing the ball with surprising power. That was Mitch.

As ESPNcricinfo reported in March 2015, the coach called Mitch over and asked him to have a bowl.

"I'm a keeper, I don't bowl," Mitch replied.

D'Costa asked him to have a try-out in

the nets, anyway.

Mitch had bowled a bit when he played for Berala Sports but that now felt like a long time ago. His bowling was rough and ready. However, Coach D'Costa liked what he saw . . . a lot. All the raw materials were there to create a great fast bowler, he thought. He pulled Mitch aside.

"Do you want to make this team?"

"I'd love to, Coach."

"Okay," said D'Costa. "That's the end of your wicketkeeping. I'm going to teach you how to bowl."

D'Costa and the other coaches at Western Suburbs helped build Mitch's bowling action from scratch. It took an entire winter at an indoor bowling school. Mitch was taught the basics of gripping and bowling the ball. He was then given four big baskets of balls and told to bowl them all, taking just a single step before releasing the ball.

The following week, he was given the same task but off two steps, then three the following week, and so on. Over time, Mitch developed a smooth run up, athletic leap and a whiplike bowling action that meant he could bowl with good speed.

Wicketkeeping was in the past, fast bowling was now his future. Within two years, he was bowling at 130–135 kilometres per hour and getting picked for the New South Wales Under-17s team. He now added a new cricketing hero – Pakistan fast bowling legend, Wasim Akram.

Mitch grew quickly in his mid-to-late teens. This meant that his young frame couldn't always put up with the workload of a pace bowler and he suffered injuries. At one point, he strained muscles in his side and had to miss a lot of cricket. Then, when he returned, eager to play, he strained the muscles on his other side! It was very frustrating. But his coach was sure of his discipline and reliability throughout, and was confident that Mitchell would make the grade.

After high school, Mitch was delighted to gain a 'rookie' development contract with New South Wales. It involved studying one year of sports science at university, followed by heading north to Queensland to train and learn at the Australian Cricket Centre of Excellence in Brisbane.

This finishing school for young cricketers has helped produce some of Australia's finest players, including Ricky Ponting, Michael Clarke and Mitch's wicketkeeping hero Adam Gilchrist, so he was thrilled to attend. He soaked up all the advice and knowledge on offer.

In March 2009, Mitch walked out onto neatly trimmed turf of the SCG – the Sydney Cricket Ground – to play for the New South Wales first XI in the Sheffield Shield for the first time.

This is Australia's national competition for its six states and Mitch was one of two young New South Wales players making debuts. The other was batter David Warner.

Mitch only took two wickets in this end of season game, but during the next season (2009–10) he took 21, including 5 for 74 versus Queensland. He and another Western Suburbs player, batter Phil Hughes, had big seasons. One of his highlights was the match against Victoria, where he snapped up four wickets and scored 54 not out – his first half century in first-class cricket.

Mitch also performed well in limited over matches, so much so that in October 2010, he found himself on a plane bound to India. He was flying out to join Australia's ODI squad – a huge thrill.

"It was my first time in India, and it was all new," he recalled in an interview with

Becoming a Bowler

Inside Cricket in February 2016. "It was a huge eye-opener, culturally."

The ODI and Test players intermingled so Mitch got the chance to mix and train with legends of the game like Ricky Ponting, Steve Smith and Mitchell Johnson. Far from being aloof, they were friendly and shared jokes with the new young fast bowler.

"I'd been watching this bloke on television play cricket for years," gushed Mitch about Ponting in his *Inside Cricket* interview. "It was fantastic. As a new kid coming in, it was like a family."

Mitch's debut for Australia on 20 October 2010 didn't go as he hoped, though. He didn't get to bat as Michael Clarke and Cameron White scored 200 between them and ensured Australia posted a reasonable total. When Australia fielded, Mitch didn't take a wicket or a catch. To make matters worse, Saurabh Tiwary hit the winning runs off Mitch's bowling, blasting two fours in succession as India overhauled Australia's score of 289.

"The only way is up," he probably imagined as he trudged off the field.

Two weeks later, he had a chance to put things right. He was back in Australia at the famous Gabba cricket ground in Brisbane. Mitch was fired up and bowled really well. A speedy delivery clipped the bat then cannoned into the base of Sri Lankan batter Angelo Mathews' leg stump.

OUT! Mitch had his first ODI wicket.

His pace and sharp bounce saw him take a further three wickets to end with brilliant bowling figures of 4 for 27. He had helped bowl Sri Lanka out for a mere 115, giving Australia an easy victory. Mitch was elated and would have enjoyed the TV commentator's words on his first wicket when he got to watch the highlights.

"There's number one. We're gonna see a lot more of this boy. He is talented."

⭐ CHAPTER 5 ⭐

Bagging a Baggy Green

When the Australian Test team line up for an official photo, one thing marks them out from other Test cricket sides – and it's on their heads. The distinctive dark myrtle-green cap, made of merino wool, has been worn by Aussie cricketers for over 100 years. Known as the 'baggy green', it's now an Aussie icon.

In the 1990s, Australian cricket captain Mark Taylor insisted all his team wore theirs when fielding in the first session of a Test match. The captains who followed him – Steve Waugh, Ricky Ponting and Michael Clarke – also built up the importance of the hat as a symbol. Waugh introduced a ceremony where a former captain or famous ex-player handed debutantes their own baggy green, fresh out of the box.

Some baggy greens have sold for a lot of money. One belonging to famous Australian batter Sir Donald Bradman sold at auction for a cool 425,000 Australian dollars (just under £220,000). Seventeen years later, Shane Warne auctioned his baggy green to raise money for bushfire victims. It fetched over a million – 1,007,500 Australian dollars to be precise. That's around £519,000!

Growing up, Mitch had dreamed of bagging his own baggy green and playing for the Australian Test cricket side. Just before flying out to India in 2010, former teammates, he and his former teammate, Alyssa Healy, had turned their friendship into a romance. In January 2011, Mitch was delighted for his girlfriend when she got her baggy green cap. He watched her Test debut from the stands of the Bankstown Oval in Sydney.

After the day's play, when Alyssa tried to put her baggy green cap on Mitch's head, he wouldn't let her. She tried again. He refused. As the pair told the *Sydney Morning Herald* in June 2020, Mitch had said, "Alyssa, it's not mine, it's special, and I'd love to get one of my own one day, but that's yours."

At the time, Mitch was still swallowing the disappointment of getting close to the Test squad a few months earlier. After strong performances in the Sheffield Shield, he had been called up to play for Australia A against England before the 2010–11 Ashes series. A really good game could mean promotion to the Test squad.

However, Mitch suffered a muscle strain

a week before the game and couldn't play cricket for four weeks. He'd missed out and was down, but his father and New South Wales coaches just urged him to continue improving. He was young and talented and was very likely to get further chances.

Later that year, Mitch was playing well in the Sheffield Shield and in one day games as well. In November 2011, on two occasions he took five wickets in an innings, both against Queensland. People were talking about the tall, young, fast left-arm bowler and it was no surprise that he was again selected for Australia A, this time to play against New Zealand.

Mitch and James Pattinson were the pick of the team's bowlers in the first innings, grabbing seven wickets between them. In reply, the formidable Brendon McCullum pummelled 146 runs, including six sixes. McCullum in full attack mode was a frightening sight!

In the second innings, Mitch got McCullum out for just five. His teammates mobbed him and patted him on the back. As the game played out to a draw, news started filtering through the ground. Ryan Harris was injured and Mitchell was joining the full Australian squad to replace him. Amazing. The news got better and better . . . He was picked to play in the first XI. Mitch was elated.

On the morning of the game, the team gathered in a circle as one of the greats of Australian cricket came to see them. Richie Benaud had been a commanding Australian captain and great spin bowler, taking 248 Test wickets. After retiring, he became the most famous TV commentator in the game. It was Richie, also from New South Wales, who handed Mitch his baggy green cap.

"That was incredible, right at the top of my memories in cricket," Mitch told the *Sydney Morning Herald* in June 2020. "I won't forget that moment for the rest of my life."

On 1 December 2011, Mitchell Starc walked out at the Gabba proudly wearing his brand-new baggy green as Australia's 425th Test cricketer. James Pattinson and David Warner were also debuting in a much-changed Australian line-up. Despite it being well into the Australian summer, it was cloudy overhead and the pitch was grassy . . . great for bowling!

Any nerves Mitch felt were eased when New Zealand won the toss and chose to bat. He would get his chance to show what he could do that morning rather than spend the day pacing around nervously in the dressing room as Australia batted.

Bagging a Baggy Green

Peter Siddle and James Pattinson opened the bowling so Mitch would have to wait just a little longer. Mitch watched Brendon McCullum smash 12 runs off fellow debut player James Pattinson's first over. Ouch! Mitch felt for 'Patto', and when he came on to bowl in the seventh over to McCullum, he just hoped he didn't get the same treatment.

Mitch wasted his first ball; it drifted down the leg side. The second however cut back in. It caught McCullum a nasty blow on the elbow. Teammates clapped and urged him on. Balls three and four were full tosses and not great. Mitch was lucky only one was thumped to the boundary by McCullum. But his last two deliveries swung away. Mitch's bowling may have been erratic, but it was also threatening.

Into his fifth over and the moment he had dreamed of came. He bowled from around the wicket, angling the ball into Brendon McCullum, now on 34 runs. McCullum tried to cut the ball square but sent it flying straight to another debut player, David Warner, fielding at point (a part of the pitch to the right of the batter).

"It's a wonderful moment for Mitchell Starc," commentated Mark Nicholas on TV. "That is his first Test wicket."

Before the day was over, Mitch struck again, getting Jesse Ryder caught, again by David Warner.

"It's a day I'll never forget," he beamed as he talked to reporters after play. "Just to get that baggy green is a pretty proud moment for me, and to get a couple of wickets as well was fantastic."

The Starc family were all incredibly proud of Mitch – including his grandparents, Frank and

Betty Atkinson. In 2019, Frank and Betty donated merino wool from the sheep on their farm to create a new batch of baggy green caps for the next generation of Australian cricketers.

★ **CHAPTER 6** ★

A Cricketing Education

In 2012, Mitch made his third debut for
Australia, as a T20i player, but only played
four Test matches – each against different
opponents. He was just making his way in
international cricket and was in and out of
Australian sides. He found himself used as
a replacement when another bowler such as
Peter Siddle or Ryan Harris was injured, only to
be jettisoned when that player was fit again.

Mitch, though, wasn't sulking. Far from it.
He knew he had much to learn and was
absorbing every moment he spent in the

Australian squad. To be around champion cricketers and see how they train, prepare and act offered really valuable lessons.

Australia were playing a New Year's Test against India at the Sydney Cricket Ground (SCG) and Mitch wasn't picked. As he worked out in the nets, a famous ex-player and coach struck up a conversation with him. It was none other than his bowling idol, Wasim Akram.

Wasim was impressed with Mitch's bowling action, which he described to ESPNcricinfo in February 2012 as "beautiful" and "smooth". He talked to the young bowler about different angles to bowl at batters, but mostly about wrist position and the art of swing bowling.

"I told him when he comes in to bowl to the right-handers like he does normally, to flick his wrist at the last moment to gain the most swing – the snap."

A Cricketing Education

Mitch took in every word. After all, when a cricket legend with 414 Test and 502 ODI wickets talks to you, you listen! The *Sydney Morning Herald* reported how valuable Mitch had found it in January 2012: "I spent 25 minutes with him, and it was priceless."

With no Test to play, Mitch headed off for a T20 match for the Sydney Sixers in the first season of the Big Bash League – where he instantly made a mark. In just two and a half overs, he took three big wickets and was voted player of the match. A week later and Mitchell was running in to bowl at the Indian batting legend, Sachin Tendulkar.

Mitch was recalled for Australia's third Test against India. He hadn't even been born when Tendulkar made his international debut in 1989. He had since made 99 Test and ODI centuries and was on the hunt for his 100th hundred during the match when he faced Mitch.

As Mitch bounded in, he vowed to put the great advice from Wasim Akram to good effect. He released the ball with as much snap as he could muster. It was a wicked delivery. The ball swung in sharply, beat the bat and thumped into Sachin's pads.

Up went all the Australian fielders. "Howzat!" It was pretty close – but the umpire's finger went up. OUT! Watching on TV at home, Mitch's mum, Julie, leapt off the sofa and danced around her living room!

"I didn't watch Sachin walk off," Mitch admitted to reporters in the post-match interview. "I was too busy celebrating in the huddle with my mates. It was a great moment, but you move on and get more wickets."

The cricket world had certainly noticed though. Within days, Mitch's manager,

A Cricketing Education

Andrew Fraser, had been flooded with calls from overseas clubs and teams asking if Mitch was available. In May, as summer turned to autumn in Australia, Mitch decided to continue his cricket education by playing abroad and flew to England.

He signed a short-term deal with Yorkshire to play in both the County Championship and limited overs competitions. Few knew the tall Aussie bowler who had only played four Test matches, but Yorkshire coach Jason Gillespie was a former Australian fast bowler himself and thought Mitch would make a great signing.

Things went anything but smoothly at first. He arrived in England in May only to find that his work permit – paperwork that would let him play and be paid in England – wasn't correct. Mitch ended up being held at Heathrow Airport for five hours before he was deported.

Amazing Cricket Stars – Mitchell Starc

He had to fly halfway round the world back to Australia, fill in some forms, then fly all the way back again the following week. Phew! And when he returned, his Yorkshire coach decided he was too tired to make his debut.

As ESPNcricinfo reported in May 2012, Gillespie was not about to rush Starc. "We just thought it was too much of an ask [. . .] after all the issues and the amount of travel he's done."

At least Mitch was provided with a sponsored car so he could drive around. Even that had a small problem – the sponsors had painted the name 'Stac' on the side, instead of 'Starc'!

Things could only get better . . . and they did. Mitch joined a county side which contained future England stars, Joe Root and Jonny Bairstow. They nicknamed him 'Terminal' for all the flying he had done in the previous two weeks.

After years of using the Kookaburra ball in

A Cricketing Education

Australia, Mitch now had to learn how to bowl with the Dukes ball, a type of cricket ball used in England and Wales. He found the Dukes ball swung more, so he had to learn how to control it. He also sought plenty of advice from coach Gillespie and his English teammates. It was a valuable learning period, and fun, too.

His first County Championship match was at the end of May. Mitch bowled well, with figures of 2 for 64 and 3 for 50, as well as scoring 28 not out as the match was drawn. A week later, he took the first two wickets versus Glamorgan, only for the game to be washed out due to rain. Frustrating.

Mitch had better luck in the limited overs competition for Yorkshire. He played 10 matches in the Friends Life T20i competition and Yorkshire reached the final for the first time. He took 21 wickets – the most of any player – but couldn't play in the final as Australia came calling again.

He was added to the squad for an ODI series in England, but again wasn't picked to play. In a later TV interview with Fox Cricket in December 2022, he said he didn't feel settled until he'd played 25 Test matches or so.

"I guess I had to learn on my feet. I came out of wicketkeeping into bowling and it's all happened pretty quickly."

Mitch was learning that patience as well as bowling skills would be necessary for a successful career in international cricket.

CHAPTER 7

One Short

March 2013 in Mohali, India . . . and Australia's Test team were feeling the pinch. After a good start, Australia were in danger of fading away. They were 251 for six, then seven, as Peter Siddle was out for a duck off 14 balls – one of three batters to fall without scoring. Australia's innings rested on the shoulders of Steve Smith as Mitch came out to bat.

"Just hang in there and let Steve reach his ton," Mitch was probably thinking as he scratched his guard and faced his first ball. It spun out of Ravindra Jadeja's fingers, pitched and beat his bat.

Mitch, in his ninth Test match, was beaten again by the last ball of Jadeja's over, but took a liking to Bhuvneshwar Kumar's bowling at the other end. He swatted ten runs off the next over and Kumar was quickly removed from India's attack.

A few months earlier, Mitch had made 68 not out versus South Africa. That innings lasted just 43 balls and saw him bludgeon two sixes and nine fours. Here, he was more patient and played more carefully . . . well, most of the time.

Mitch reached his half century with a lovely flick off his pads for four runs – his seventh boundary of the innings. He saw off a fiery over from India's fastest bowler, Ishant Sharma, and reached 56, before Steve Smith was out for 92. Now, Mitch had to lead the batting with Nathan Lyon as his new partner.

After taking 11 runs off of one Pragyan Ojha over, Mitch cut a ball for a single to reach his highest first-class score of 69. The ball trickled away across the worn outfield.

A punched four past backward point took his score into the eighties. At the other end, Nathan Lyon was doing a great job of keeping India at bay. But after 38 balls, he had only scored five. The onus to score runs was all on Mitch.

He struck another four off Ojha to take him into the 'nervous nineties'. Mitch was starting to feel both pressure and fatigue. He had been batting for more than two hours and had faced 130 balls. He was suffering, too, from painful bone spurs – little bony lumps – on his ankle joint.

Ishant Sharma was called back into the Indian attack. He had spent a lot of time that day chasing the ball after it had raced off Mitch's bat. He was in no mood for the young Australian's innings to go on much longer. He bowled a sharp ball which Mitch hit for four.

THUMP!

He was now on 96, then 98, then 99 . . . Things were getting tense.

Michael Clarke and the rest of the Australian team were all up on their feet, eyes fixed on the action. They were urging Mitch on to score his first Test century. Surely, he could. After all, he had been so assured throughout his innings.

Ishant turned on his heels and sped in to bowl. The ball arrived, Mitch poked forward, and the ball sped into the gloves of wicketkeeper MS Dhoni. OUT!

"That really is heartbreaking," sighed the TV commentator. "He did play so well. He deserved it."

Mitch departed just one short of his maiden Test century. He'd faced 144 balls and struck 14 fours. More importantly for the team, he had taken Australia to 399 for 9, a respectable score.

One Short

Talking to reporters afterwards, Mitch was anything but down. "That was just a lot of fun to play," he smiled. "To fall one short is disappointing though, and hopefully I can get another chance one day."

In the second innings, despite the bone spurs in his ankle, Mitch set himself to bat for a long time again, to help Australia save the match. He lasted 100 balls, scoring 35 before a turning ball from Ravindra Jadeja saw him last man out, caught by Ravichandran Ashwin.

Mitch became the first tailender (a player batting ninth, tenth or eleventh) to survive 100 balls in both innings of a Test. It was little consolation as Australia lost both the game and the series. He also bowled 201 balls into the unforgiving Mohali pitch.

With the series lost, Mitch flew home so that the bone spurs could be investigated and operated on. Little did anyone know that it would be eight years before Mitch got close to making a first-class century again. This time, he was batting for New South Wales in the Australian Sheffield Shield tournament. Mitch's reaction was quite different this time to his feelings after Mohali.

New South Wales had been bowled out by Tasmania for just 64 in their first innings but had bounced back admirably. They were 522–6 with Mitch playing beautifully on 86, when captain Peter Nevill appeared on the boundary and waved the batters in. The skipper declared his team's innings over so NSW could bowl at Tasmania for 40 minutes that evening.

Mitch shook his head and marched off, annoyed at the declaration. Then he threw his bat and gloves down beside the team tent. His captain apologised to him, but when Tasmania were 26–2 at the end of the day, it looked like the captain had made the correct decision.

It was rare to see Mitch show dissent to his own team. As ESPNcricinfo reported in November 2020, his teammate Nathan Lyon said, "Starcy is the least selfish team man I've ever met. He's always about the team and always wanting the team to win."

Mitch quickly got over his disappointment and threw himself into the team cause. New South Wales completed the win the next day with Mitch and Nathan both taking three wickets each.

As of the start of 2024, Mitch was still hunting for his elusive first century, and was the fifth highest scorer of Test runs (1,992) without a century in history. He has scored 46 sixes – more than Joe Root and just four fewer than hard-hitting Jonny Bairstow.

★ CHAPTER 8 ★

World Cup Warrior

CRUNCH!

Mitch's stumps had been splattered by a fast delivery from New Zealand's premier pace bowler, Trent Boult. Australia were 106 for 9 and eventually all out for only 151.

The Auckland crowd cheered. Their team had just demolished their closest rival's batting line up in the 2015 ICC World Cup, staged jointly in New Zealand and Australia.

"Ha, ha! Terrible display from the Aussies."

"They're 150 runs short on this pitch. Beautiful!"

"This is such an easy run chase for New Zealand."

Australia had only batted for 32 of their 50 overs. It looked certain that they were going to suffer their first defeat of the tournament. Mitch, excited to be at his first ODI World Cup, had other ideas.

It had been a hard slog leading up to his first ICC World Cup. In 2014, he'd been playing in a Sheffield Shield game against South Australia, whose side included Phil Hughes, his old teammate. Hughes was struck on the side of his head below his helmet by a bouncer bowled by one of Mitch's fellow bowlers and collapsed.

Mitch visited him in hospital, but Hughes died two days later. Speaking to the press in March 2015, Mitch said, "He'll never be forgotten and he's definitely part of this World Cup squad." Mitch and the Australian team captain Michael

Clarke wore black armbands throughout the 2015 World Cup in memory of Phil.

New Zealand began their batting strongly, eager to chase down the 152 runs they needed for victory. After just three and a half overs, they were 40 for no loss. Mitch's first over was pummelled by Brendon McCullum and went for 14 runs. Ouch! With such a good start and such a low target, bowling dry to stop the run flow really wasn't an option. What Australia needed were wickets . . . and fast. Mitch responded.

Out!

Martin Guptill was forced by Mitch into chipping the ball straight to Pat Cummins, who took an easy catch. 40–1.

Out!

With the New Zealand team on 79–1, Mitch returned the favour, taking an easy catch to dismiss the mighty McCullum off Pat Cummins' bowling. McCullum had scored 50 off just 24 balls – extraordinary hitting.

Out! Out!

In a sensational fourth over of his bowling, Mitch bowled both Ross Taylor for one and Grant Elliott for a duck (no runs at all). Could Australia have a chance?

New Zealand rebuilt well. Try as they might, Australia's other quick bowlers – Mitchell Johnson, Pat Cummins and Mitchell Marsh could not grab another wicket. New Zealand reached 130 for 4. They needed just 22 runs with 30 overs left. It looked hopeless for Australia, but captain Michael Clarke brought Mitch back on. At the other end, spinner Glenn Maxwell took a wicket.

Out!

Mitch bowled a wicked bouncer at Luke Ronchi. He tried to sway out of its way, but the ball seemed to follow him, grazed his gloves and Brad Haddin caught it behind the stumps.

New Zealand were 139 for 6, then 7 as Pat Cummins struck.

Mitch began his ninth over. He had 4 for 27, but New Zealand only needed seven runs to win.

Out!

Mitch bowled an unplayable yorker – a shot that hits the pitch very near the batter. This one pitched right at the feet of Adam Milne, then thundered into the stumps, sending the middle pole flying.

In came Tim Southee to bat. New Zealand were 146 for 8 and things were getting tense.

Out!

Mitch did it again next ball. Another searing yorker cannoned into the stumps and the Australians in the crowd went wild. Southee was out first ball without scoring (a golden duck).

Trent Boult came in as New Zealand's
last batter and Mitch was on a hat-trick . . .

Ooooh!

Mitch bowled another fabulous delivery,
homing in on the stumps, but Boult defended
it stoutly. The final ball of the over was kept out,
too. And when Kane Williamson hit a six off
Pat Cummins ball in the next over, the game
was up. New Zealand had won.

Mitch's amazing figures of 6 for 28 had got
close to single-handedly winning the match
for Australia. As Cricket Australia reported
online after the match, Australian captain
Michael Clarke said, "Starc is a genius." This
exciting, closely fought game had ignited the
competition and it was no surprise that the
two teams most on form met again in the final.
Before then, Mitch took 4 for 14 versus Scotland
and two Indian wickets in the semi-final to take

his World Cup tally to 20.

Mitch's father, Paul, had stopped coming to watch his son play live in 2011. Every time he turned up, it seemed his son wasn't picked, and if he was, he didn't play well. Yet the times he watched the matches at home on TV, he played brilliantly. Paul Starc felt he was a jinx.

With Australia now in the final, Mitch wanted his father at the biggest game of his career, so he made arrangements then called him. He told Cricket Australia's online site in June 2023, "I told him I'd booked the flights, booked the hotel. He had to come."

On 29 March, Paul Starc joined a further 93,012 spectators, all packed into the giant oval bowl that forms the Melbourne Cricket Ground. New Zealand won the toss and chose to bat. The ball was thrown to Mitch to bowl first. Could he use his deadly yorkers to remove

New Zealand's danger man, Brendon McCullum?

After two balls bowled to Martin Guptill, New Zealand scored a run and Brendon McCullum was now on strike (at the end of the pitch facing the bowler).

Mitch bowled a 149 kilometres per hour delivery that pitched just outside off stump (the stump furthest away from the batter's body). McCullum swung hard but missed. Interesting . . .

The New Zealander charged down the pitch at Mitch's next ball and missed again. Out in the stands, the crowd were excited.

"Oooooh. Come on Aussie!"

"Baz is really charged up tonight."

"But Starc is bowling fast and well. Something's gotta give."

Mitch's third ball to McCullum was an absolute beauty of a yorker. It was fast, swung in late and McCullum had no answer. As it thundered into the stumps, the ground erupted.

OUT!

Mitch raced off, powered by the roar of the crowd. He was mobbed by teammates. They all knew how important that first wicket was. Up in the stands, Paul Starc thanked his son for arranging the travel and tickets. Where else would he want to be than here on a night like this!

New Zealand were 1 for 1 with their good-luck charm McCullum gone. They never really recovered, making only 183. Australia powered home with more than 16 overs remaining and became World Cup champions.

"This victory is dedicated to our little brother, Phillip Hughes," said an emotional Michael Clarke to reporters after the game.

Mitch was named player of the tournament. He had taken the most wickets (22), each

costing an average of only 10.18 runs.
Phenomenal.

After the World Cup win, Paul Starc abandoned his plans to only watch his son on TV. He started attending every match Mitch played! At the games he formed good friendships with two other proud fathers of fast bowlers, Trevor Hazlewood and Peter Cummins. The trio could be seen taking their seats for the match or after play, sitting in the Australian dressing room together.

Mitch and Australia were keen for a repeat performance at the next World Cup in 2019. An impressive seven wins propelled them to the semi-final, including victories over favourites, England (Mitch taking 4 for 43) and New Zealand (5 for 26). England gained their revenge, though, in the semi-final. Australia were out – England had won.

Mitch's only consolation was that he'd taken a record 27 wickets, the most of any bowler at any World Cup.

★ CHAPTER 9 ★

The 'Stealy' Cup

Back in Australia, after the 2015 World Cup
triumph, Mitch celebrated with friends a lot.
Alyssa, his girlfriend, thought they should be
spending a little more time together, especially
after months apart. One day, after Alyssa
headed off to the gym, Mitch travelled into
Sydney to buy something. He had a plan.

A short while later, the pair went on holiday to
the beautiful Hayman Island in the Great
Barrier Reef. It was the perfect place to relax . . .
only Mitch couldn't. He was terribly nervous.
On a hike to the island's cliffs one day, he was

particularly anxious. It was only when Alyssa sat down to admire the view that the reason became clear. Mitch pulled out the object he'd bought in Sydney weeks earlier – a diamond engagement ring! In an interview with the *Sydney Morning Herald* in June 2020, the couple recalled the event:

Mitch: "I nearly fell off the face of a cliff getting down on one knee."

Alyssa: "I said yes, and then we had to get off the cliff face before it got dark."

The couple got married the following year in Sydney. Amongst the guests were fellow Aussie bowlers Nathan Lyon, Josh Hazlewood and Pat Cummins, as well as some of Mitch and Alyssa's New South Wales teammates.

Mitch's best man at the wedding, Ash Squire, was Alyssa's batting coach. He owned an indoor cricket school and Alyssa and Mitch thought it would be fun to head down and have a bat and a bowl. But the pair were so competitive that staff there told them off for trying to smash the ball as hard as they could.

A few months after their wedding, the couple were both making headlines on the cricket pitch. Mitch, having returned from a long injury, took 24 wickets whilst touring Sri Lanka – the most by an overseas bowler in a three Test series in Asia. In the second Sri Lankan Test, he took five wickets in the first innings to pass 100 wickets in Tests. In the second innings, he went even better, with amazing bowling figures of 6 for 40, giving him match figures of 11 for 94 – awesome!

Australia and Sri Lanka contested a One Day International series straight after the Tests and Mitch continued his record-breaking form. In his 52nd ODI game, he became the fastest player to take 100 ODI wickets, beating a record that had stood for 19 years.

A little later in 2016, Alyssa 'borrowed' one of Mitch's cricket bats and sawed a piece off the handle ("It was no good to me after that," noted Mitch, as reported in the *Daily Mail* in July 2023). She used it to great effect in the Women's Big Bash League, striking the competition's fastest 50, off just 38 balls. Alyssa also won five player of the match awards and launched the Sydney Sixers into the top spot. Champions!

Mitch is often in the stands cheering Alyssa on when she's taking the opposition apart with her destructive batting, or giving coaching clinics and advice to up-and-coming women fast bowlers.

In 2020, he gained permission to leave Australia's tour of South Africa so that he could see Alyssa play in the final of the T20i World Cup in Australia. As reported by ESPNcricinfo in March 2020, Mitch's coach, Justin Langer, said,

"It's a once in a lifetime chance, so we were happy to allow him to return home."

As soon as Australia's women had made it to the T20i final, Mitch jumped in a car, drove a few hours to Johannesburg Airport, flew 14 hours from South Africa to Sydney, got back home, dropped off his bags then travelled back to the airport to hop on a plane to get to the final in Melbourne. Phew! It proved worth it when Alyssa pummelled 75 off just 39 balls to help Australia to victory.

"The girls can be really proud," said Mitch afterwards, in the couple's June 2020 interview with the *Sydney Morning Herald*. "They had the world captivated."

Mitch and Alyssa's competitive streaks extend beyond cricket. They battle to be the winner at many other things, from golf to computer games.

Mitch's introduction to golf came early and

was due to his father's love of the game –
Paul Starc had always been an avid golfer.

"Just being outdoors, in pairs, golf became
the perfect tool to unwind away from the
cricket field," noted Mitch in a November 2022
interview about himself and Alyssa in *Australian
Golf Digest* magazine. "We call ourselves golf
tragics. It's all we spend our money on – golf
clubs, balls and clothing."

Pride of place amongst Mitch and Alyssa's
many cricket trophies is a bronze jug the couple
bought themselves. This is the Starc-Healy (or
'Stealy') Cup – the golf trophy they compete
head-to-head for every year. Mitch won the
Stealy Cup in its third year but otherwise
Alyssa has dominated and been champ
pretty much every other time.

Mind you, Mitch did get to add another
trophy to their haul come the end of 2016. In

recognition of his 50 Test wickets, he was given the highly prized Australia's Men's Test Player of the Year award.

★ CHAPTER 10 ★

The Toughest of Times

On 6 January 2020, Mitch took three New Zealand wickets and Nathan Lyon five as Australia bowled the Kiwis out for 136 and won the final Test match of the Trans-Tasman Series by a whopping 279 runs.

Little did Mitch, Nathan or the rest of the team know that it would be their last Test match until 17 December. The COVID-19 pandemic took hold and cricket was cancelled in much of the world.

When Australia's Tests resumed with a four-Test series at home against India just before Christmas, players had to live and train in bio-bubbles. This often meant being quarantined alone in hotel rooms for many days after arriving in a new country, then only being allowed to train and play, and not being allowed to go out and mix with people. Games were held in empty stadiums; the lack of atmosphere was spooky.

Some players spent many months in bio-bubbles during the pandemic. "It's not a sustainable lifestyle," Mitch said in an interview, reported on the Cricket Australia website. "You're living in a hotel room with zero outside contact. Some guys haven't seen families or their kids for a long time . . . It's tough going."

When back at home, Mitch and Alyssa put together a home gym and worked out a lot. Mitch always lost weight during a cricket season due to the heavy workload on fast bowlers.

The Toughest of Times

So, he tried to bulk up – as he told Cricket Australia's online site in August 2020, he put on five kilograms of muscle during the middle of the year. The aim was to make him feel stronger for those long innings where he had to bowl three, four or five spells. Then it was off to England in September, back in a bio-bubble, first at Southampton for a series of T20i games, then up to Manchester for three One Day Internationals.

During this already difficult period, Mitch and his family received terrible news. His father, Paul, was diagnosed with cancer. Mitch wanted to be by his father's side every day, but Paul wanted Mitch to continue playing for Australia. This would give Paul something to watch on television and look forward to whilst he rested and recovered from bouts of treatment.

Mitch followed his father's wishes, but he travelled back to Sydney whenever he could during late 2020 and early 2021 to see Paul. With travel frequently restricted due to COVID-19, this was often difficult. In December 2020, he pulled out of two T20i matches against India, but later that month returned to Australia's Test side when they took on India in a four-match series.

Mitch only took three wickets in the last two of the four Tests and was heavily criticised by some pundits and ex-players. None of them knew what he was going through with his family. It was only when speaking on Australian TV network Channel 7 a year later that Mitch admitted, "I didn't play the cricket I wanted to and, at certain stages, I probably didn't want to play cricket at all."

Mitch's father died in February 2021. "I was grateful I got to see him the day before he passed away, but you always want more time," Mitch said later, as reported by Cricket Australia online in June 2023. Instead of a traditional funeral, Paul Starc had wanted a celebration to be held at the Cumberland Country Golf Club outside Sydney – his favourite place to play.

When Paul's partner, Liz, was going through his things, she found a large collection of newspaper clippings. They were all about Mitch. They documented his cricket career going all the way back to when he joined New South Wales as a junior. Mitch had no idea about the collection and was deeply touched.

With the support of Alyssa, close friends and his family, Mitch eased back into cricket. He played seven T20i and One Day International games in the West Indies in July and seven more T20is in Abu Dhabi and Dubai in October and November, still in bio-bubbles.

Finally, a home series came round with the 2021–2022 Ashes versus England. Starved of international cricket in their country for a while, Australian fans were keen to see their team make an impact against their fierce rivals, the 'Poms'.

The first ball in an Ashes series has developed its own myths and meanings to fans. On some occasions, it seems to summarise the rest of the series that follows. For example, in 2023, England opener Zak Crawley surprisingly hit the first ball to the boundary. It seemed to signify England's new fearless, attacking approach, known as 'Bazball'. Back in 2006, England fast bowler Steve Harmison, known as 'Harmie', bowled such a wide first ball that it ended up at second slip, ten metres to the right of the wicketkeeper! England went on to get thrashed.

Standing at the top of his mark at the Gabba on 17 December 2021, Mitch took a deep breath. He banished any negative thoughts from his mind – he certainly didn't want to bowl a shocker. Facing him was England opening batter, Rory Burns.

Mitch sprinted in, leapt and released the ball. It angled across Burns and swung in a little, very late. Burns fell to the offside as the ball thundered into the base of his leg stump. OUT!

The TV commentary team, who included Mitch's teen cricket idol, Adam Gilchrist, couldn't believe it.

"Ooh, bowled him!"

"Immediate breakthrough. The roar goes up."

"It's all happening at the Gabba."

"Couldn't be any better for the Aussies!"

It was the first time since 1936 that a batter had been out first ball of an Ashes series.

Mitch had set the tone. By the end of the day's play, a sorry looking England were 147 for 9. They lost the match and the series comprehensively 4–0 with Mitch taking 19 wickets.

At the Australian Cricket Awards held just after the series, Mitch won not one, but two major prizes. He was voted Men's ODI Player of the Year and received the coveted Allan Border Medal for the country's most outstanding male cricketer of 2021. His father, Paul, would have been very proud.

CHAPTER 11

Karachi to Christchurch

Mitch and Alyssa had already got used to being in different places as they travelled the world with their respective Australian teams. Some years, they only spent a total of three or so months together.

"Even in the Australian summer it's sporadic," Mitch said in a June 2020 interview with the *Sydney Morning Herald*. "We're never at home for more than a couple of days between games." In March 2022, they found themselves away again on different continents, this time 13,000 kilometres apart.

Alyssa was taking part in the ICC Women's World Cup held in six cities in New Zealand. Alyssa had won the competition in 2013 but, like Mitchell in 2019, had suffered an agonising semi-final defeat in the 2017 World Cup. She was aching to lift the trophy one more time.

Whilst Alyssa flew across the Tasman Sea to New Zealand, Mitch was packing his bags for Pakistan after a fun training camp in Melbourne. At the camp, the bowlers had to practise all sorts of different deliveries and tactics, because they didn't know what sort of pitches they would be playing on in Pakistan.

Pakistan had only recently returned to hosting Test matches and ODIs after a terrorist attack on the Sri Lankan team bus in 2009 halted tours there. For more than a decade, they had to play their home games in the United Arab Emirates. Mitchell had never played a Test in Pakistan before. None of the team had! The last time an Australian Test side had toured the country was 24 years previously. Many of Pakistan's 220 million-strong population are massive cricket fans, and they couldn't wait to see their team taking on Australia at home.

Mitchell was nervous but excited at visiting the home country of his cricketing idol, Wasim Akram. In an earlier interview with *Herald Sun* in August 2016, he'd called Wasim "an absolute genius," and said that "he set the standard for left-arm fast bowling. If I could be even half the bowler that he was, that would be great."

The Australian team were to be guarded around the clock with the sort of security normally arranged for visiting royalty and government heads. Travelling from their first hotel in Islamabad to the cricket stadium in Rawalpindi involved an armoured convoy

of vehicles surrounding the team bus,
whilst army helicopters whirred overhead.

After all that build up and tension, the first
Test was sadly a bit of a disappointment for both
teams. Try as they might, Mitch, Pat Cummins
and Josh Hazlewood could get nothing out of
the pitch. Mitch bowled 31 tiring overs and didn't
get a single wicket. Australia's main spin bowler,
Nathan Lyon, took one wicket for 236 runs. Mind
you, the Pakistan bowlers didn't fare much better.
The bat dominated the ball so much that the
match ended with only 14 wickets taken in total
and with Pakistan on 252–0 in their second innings.

At least Mitch could be cheered by events
that day in New Zealand. Alyssa had been made
player of the match as Australia had defeated
the Pakistan women's ODI team comfortably in
their second game of the tournament.

Mitchell and the rest of the men's team moved

on to Karachi. There, despite a threatening burst by Mitch (taking 3 for 29), Pakistan held on. Mitch's wickets included the 15th time he'd had a chance in international cricket to bowl a hat-trick of wickets. Not that he fretted about it; his mind was already focusing on the third and final Test. Despite long, sapping spells of bowling on pitches for little reward, Mitch was ready for the final match.

The third Test progressed at a quicker pace than the first two games. Australia scored 391 in their first innings and Pakistan were cruising in reply, passing 240 for the loss of just three wickets . . . until Pat Cummins tossed the ball to Mitch. In a few overs, he ripped through the Pakistan middle order.

First to go was Fawad Alam. Mitch bowled a fizzing delivery that landed on a good length but nipped back to go through the 'gate' –

the gap between pad and bat – to smash
into the stumps. Fawad was out, bowled for 13.
Mitch had bowled 15½ overs so far and
had only given away 19 runs. Incredible.

"Cleaned him up! What a delivery!" roared
the TV commentator.

Then, a few balls later, Mohammad Rizwan
could do nothing about a superb delivery from
Mitch. He managed to reverse swing the ball,
just like his idol, Wasim Akram. The ball beat
Rizwan's bat and clattered into the top of
off-stump. Pakistan were now 256 for 5
and in trouble.

The few Australians in the crowd were
getting excited. Could an Aussie win be on
the cards?

"Howzat! Mitchell, you little ripper!"

"What a ball from Starc! Again!"

"He and Cummins are simply phenomenal."

The team captain now joined in the fun; Cummins grabbed three before Mitchell took the prized wicket of Pakistan captain and star batter, Babar Azam, out leg before wicket (LBW). In came Pakistan's last batter, Naseem Shah, but he only lasted four balls until Mitch sent another rocket into the stumps. Pakistan were 268 all out, and Pat and Mitch had taken seven wickets for just 20 runs between them.

As the game continued, Mitch and Pat's spells proved decisive. Australia won the game by 115 runs and recorded a famous series victory. Mitch and the rest of the side celebrated their win the same day Alyssa scored 129 off 107 balls to help her side into the Women's World Cup final.

Mitch dashed to the airport. He made the 28-hour trip from Lahore to Christchurch to support Alyssa and the rest of the Aussie women's team. He took his seat in the scenic Hagley Oval in Christchurch for the final and watched on, open-mouthed, as Alyssa wowed the crowd and led Australia to victory. Her blistering 170 was the highest World Cup final score by a male or female cricketer. The previous highest was 149 by Mitch's childhood hero, Adam Gilchrist.

Alyssa was now a two-time World Cup winner and both she and Mitch were World Cup record holders: Mitch for the most wickets at a tournament, and Alyssa for her 170 and making the most runs at a tournament (509). What a pair!

CHAPTER 12

The Big 300

Just like Alyssa, Mitch fancied winning another World Cup, but there was a lot of important cricket before the next tournament in India in October and November 2023. This included the ICC World Test Championship (WTC) and an Ashes series in England.

The World Test Championship began in 2019 and was now in its second edition (2021–23). The nine Test match nations (Australia, Bangladesh, England, India, New Zealand, Pakistan, South Africa, Sri Lanka and the West Indies) play matches against each other over a two year or so period. After the matches are completed, the top two teams play each other in a single Test match to determine who would become world champions.

Australia had agonisingly missed out on the final in the 2019–21 competition. They were docked points for bowling their overs too slowly and narrowly missed making the top two teams. Pat Cummins and the rest of the side were determined not to miss out again.

The Test series in Pakistan that Australia had just won counted to their tally – Mitch's team were putting in a string of impressive performances away from home.

Their road to the 2023 WTC final had begun brilliantly at home with their 4–0 thrashing of England. Mitch had created one of the Ashes' most iconic moments by taking Rory Burns' wicket with the very first ball of the series.

Then followed victory in Pakistan and a drawn series in Sri Lanka, with Mitch taking four Sri Lankan wickets in the second Test.

Heading back to Australia, West Indies were beaten before South Africa visited for a three-match contest. During this series, Mitch reached a milestone. In the first Test, he clean bowled Rassie van der Dussen with a wonderful delivery that nipped back. It was his 300th Test wicket – only four other Australian fast bowlers have ever achieved that feat.

"Three hundred!" bellowed the TV commentator. "There it is! He joins the greats. His teammates are around him. The crowd is up."

Australia won the match in just two days and captain Pat Cummins praised Mitch's achievement in the post-match press conference:

"It's huge. I've seen him a lot of times mending scars and bruises and blisters in the changing room. You see the toil behind the actual wickets and performances, so it puts him right up into the upper echelon of great Aussie bowlers."

Mitch enjoyed the praise but knew not to get too pleased with himself. As an experienced player, he knew how cricket had a habit of providing lows as well as highs. And a couple of weeks later at the Boxing Day Test in Melbourne, Mitch came a cropper, suffering yet another injury . . . a nasty one. Whilst fielding at long-on, a part of the pitch behind the bowler, he sprinted round to reach the ball struck by South African batter Marco Jansen. He dived full length, but only got his middle finger behind the ball.

He grimaced in pain, lay on the ground and signalled for the physio. On trotted Nick Jones, who examined the injury. Mitch had ripped the tendon from the bone of his middle finger of his bowling hand.

Despite the detached tendon, Mitch batted bravely to score ten runs, and then bowled 18 overs to help defeat South Africa and win the series. Mitch had little feeling in his finger but told reporters afterwards that it actually helped him not grip the ball too hard, so he gained good swing as a result.

As ESPNcricinfo reported in December 2022, he joked, "I might see if they want to leave it detached for a bit longer."

However, the injury turned out to be no laughing matter. His 'reward' for playing on in the Boxing Day Test was to start the New Year with his hand in a brace as he could no longer move the damaged finger at all. He missed the start of the next series, away in India, and when he played in the last two Tests was roundly criticised for taking just two wickets (at a cost of 132 runs).

Years earlier, Mitch would have found the comments upsetting, but he had since learned not to let barbs from the media bother him. The only words that mattered, he believed, were from his coaches, teammates and family. As the *Times of India* reported in June 2023, Mitch said, "If I'm the whipping boy sometimes, that's fine. I'm certainly more comfortable now in my own skin."

He chose not to take up an offer to play in the IPL. As a star player, he might have received a big fee, but he wanted to focus on the huge year of cricket ahead for Australia.

"The money's nice," he said in June 2023, "but I'd love to play a hundred Test matches. Whether I get there or not, I don't know, but that would be a nice one to tick off. Hopefully, there's a little bit left in me."

The Big 300

Australia lost the Test series in India but still qualified for the WTC final, to be played at the Oval in London in June 2023. Of the 19 WTC Tests Australia had played, they won 11, drew five and only lost three – a terrific record.

Mitch opened the bowling in the final, but after just two overs was replaced by Scott Boland. Twelve overs of fielding followed before Pat Cummins called him back into the attack. Virat Kohli was at the crease on 14 and Australia knew that getting him out before he scored big was a priority.

Mitch pounded in hard. He wanted Kohli's wicket badly. He bent his back and launched the ball straight and a little short of the batter. As the ball pitched, it reared up sharply. Virat tried to veer out of its way, but the ball caught his glove and soared upwards. Steve Smith leapt and flung his arms up high above his head to grab the ball. Superb bowling. Great catch!

"That's a brute of a delivery!" cried an Australian fan in the crowd.

"What a snorter!" yelled another.

"India 71–4. Starc, you beauty!" bellowed someone else.

All around the ground, pockets of supporters dressed in green and gold cheered. Some waved inflatable kangaroo mascots – especially when India finished their innings and were 173 runs behind. Mitch had nabbed a second wicket, that of Mohammed Shami.

Shami and Kohli combined to get their revenge on Mitch in Australia's second innings. He was batting well, armed with a secret weapon – one of his wife's cricket bats. Alyssa's bats were a little lighter than Mitch's and he'd been using it secretly for seven months, starting with the Test series against South Africa.

The Big 300

Alyssa's bat and Mitch's skill had helped put on almost 100 runs with Alex Carey. As Mitch cruised from 20 to 30 to 40, he started eyeing his eleventh Test half-century – his last had been scored way back in 2019. But a good ball from Mohammed Shami flew off his bat straight to Virat Kohli, fielding at first slip, behind the batter. Curses!

Still, Australia were able to set India a formidable total of 444 runs to win. It was simply too big a target. Scott Boland took three wickets, Mitch took two, and spinner Nathan Lyon nabbed four, including the last wicket of the match. As the final catch was taken, the whole team ran onto the pitch into a tight huddle. Nathan Lyon hugged Mitch then Mitch hugged Pat Cummins before going to console the two Indian batters.

"We had to be patient to get the breakthroughs,"

Mitch said to reporters after the match. "Two fantastic sides, fantastic cricket to watch, we're going to enjoy this as a group."

Australia were World Test Champions.

⭐ CHAPTER 13 ⭐

Mitch v Bazball

Normally, when one competition or series ends and another starts, the Australian team have to board flights and travel a long way. Mitch has clocked up hundreds of thousands of air miles flying round the world to play for Australia. After the WTC Final, however, he and the rest of the team just hopped on the team coach and headed up the M40 motorway for the short trip from London to Birmingham.

Good job too, as the next challenge began four days later – the 73rd Ashes series, pitching Australia against their oldest foes, England.

Amazing Cricket Stars - Mitchell Starc

Mitch's old batting opponent, Brendon McCullum, was now England's head coach. He and captain Ben Stokes were pioneering an exciting brand of fearless, attacking cricket. They had defeated New Zealand, South Africa, chased down a huge target to beat India, and then gone to Pakistan and won 3–0 – an unheard-of margin. The media had nicknamed Baz and Ben's fast-scoring tactics 'Bazball'. Millions of cricket fans were fascinated to see if it could work against the Aussies.

As the squad prepared at the Edgbaston Cricket Ground in Birmingham for the first Test, the big news was that Mitch had not been selected. Scott Boland and Josh Hazlewood were playing instead. Was he injured? Was he furious at the news? No, on both counts. When Mitch was interviewed, he sounded calm – as the *Independent* reported in June 2023, he said,

Mitch v Bazball

"I have been around long enough, been dropped enough. Probably been dropped the most in this squad so it is not something new for me. It probably won't be the last time either."

The next game was at Lord's, renowned by players the world over for its history as well as the great grub served to the cricketers who play there. Mitch hoped to be picked, but quipped to reporters in June 2023, "If I get a chance, it'll be exciting. If not, the lunches are pretty good!"

Despite Australia winning the first Test, Mitch was recalled for the second. He responded with six wickets as Australia won again and news headlines praised his performance.

England bounced back in the third Test held at Headingley, Leeds. They squeezed Australia into mistakes and were set a gettable target of 251 runs to win the game. It would take something special to give Australia a chance and it was Mitch who stepped up . . .

Out!

Ben Duckett was trapped LBW by an in-swinging delivery from Mitch. England were 42 for 1.

Out!

A rocket from Mitch whizzed straight through Moeen Ali's defences and smashed the stumps.

England lost two further wickets, but travelled past 150 runs. Their dangerous middle order players like Harry Brook and captain Ben Stokes were starting to tick. Surely it was all over for Australia? Pat Cummins signalled to Mitch to begin a new spell from the Kirkstall Lane end of the ground.

Out!

Ben Stokes was gone, beaten by a leg side delivery which he glanced to Australia's wicketkeeper, Alex Carey. Mitch high-fived

Steve Smith and then other members of the team who raced in to congratulate him. That was a BIG wicket.

Out!

Jonny Bairstow followed in Mitch's next over as the ball cannoned into the off and middle stumps. England were now 171 for 6, and still 80 runs away from victory.

Chance!

Mitch's ball caught the top edge of Harry Brook's bat and flew high into the Leeds sky . . . Mitch started running to catch it, head up, following the ball's path. He didn't see Pat Cummins doing the same and the pair collided. CRUNCH! Fortunately, Pat kept a tight grip on the ball as it fell and the pair smiled and hugged.

OUT!

Mitch had taken 5 for 78 but try as Australia might, they couldn't bowl England out and lost the match. The fourth Test was a draw, but Mitch injured his shoulder diving to stop the ball and had to leave the field.

Alarmed Australian fans relaxed when they heard Mitch talking afterwards. As ESPNcricinfo reported in July 2023, he said, "Just a bit of discomfort there . . . Nothing major and I'm still able to bowl and do what I need to do."

Australia still led 2–1 going into the fifth and final Test at the Oval in London. With his left shoulder strapped up, Mitch still managed to run in and bowl with pace and skill. He dismissed Ben Stokes for just three runs with a ball that knocked the off stump clean out of the ground – always a great sight for a fast bowler.

"Bowled him. What a beauty! That is a corker!" purred Sky TV commentator, Ian Ward.

He then snared Harry Brook, Chris Woakes and Stuart Broad in quick succession. Mitch's four wickets really slowed England down and he repeated the feat in the second innings, taking four for 100. But his efforts weren't enough to stop England winning the match and levelling the series.

The 2023 Ashes were a cracking series of matches for cricket fans, but exhausting for the players. England had pushed them incredibly close, but Australia could celebrate as they had kept the Ashes for another two years.

Mitch ended the series as its top wicket-taker with 23, ahead of Stuart Broad and Pat Cummins. He had proven to his critics that he was still a top Test match fast bowler. With the next ICC World Cup looming, could he still do it in ODIs as well?

★ CHAPTER 14 ★

World Cup Hurry Up

Mitch cursed as he bowled Australia's first ball of their 2023 ICC World Cup campaign. He had sent it too much down the leg side and the umpire signalled a wide. India now needed only 198 to win and he had to bowl the ball again.

This time, it was better – a full delivery that India's captain Rohit Sharma just got his bat down on in time. The next couple of balls were decent too as Mitch searched for some swing. Rohit managed a leg bye (when a batter scores an extra run after the ball deflects off their leg), bringing Ishan Kishan up the wicket to face his first ball. Some of the 33,000 Chennai crowd murmured.

"Starc looks fired up. He could take a wicket any ball."

"Without his 28 runs, Australia's position would be hopeless."

"But Ishan always scores runs fast."

"If the Aussies don't get him quick, he'll punish them."

Mitch bounded in and released the ball. As it sailed wide of the off stump, Ishan took a meaty swipe. But the ball swung, caught the edge of his bat and flew straight into the big hands of bowler Cameron Green at first slip. OUT! For a golden duck.

Mitch had struck again in the first over of an innings and celebrated with his teammates.

"Good on yer, Mitch."

"Great ball! Swing!"

World Cup Hurry Up

It was Mitch's 50th World Cup wicket. What's more, he was the quickest to reach that milestone, taking just 19 innings to do so.

Josh Hazlewood then chipped in with two early wickets, but India pressed on smoothly. In front of a passionate home crowd, Virat Kohli and KL Rahul batted beautifully. Mitch bowled eight overs but couldn't grab his 51st World Cup wicket and India reached their target with plenty of balls to spare.

Next up was South Africa. Mitch's captain, Pat Cummins, won the toss and asked South Africa to bat, but things didn't go to plan. Mitch bowled tidily but by the time he took any wickets (two in one over), South Africa had already passed 300 runs. Australia were blown away in reply, only scoring 177 all out. Mitch's 27 runs made him the team's second highest scorer.

Two games, two defeats. Australia were on

the ropes. It was only seismic shocks such as Afghanistan beating England that kept all the media attention from focusing on Australia and their problems.

Captain Cummins insisted that Australia would bounce back. Wins over Sri Lanka, Pakistan and the Netherlands helped restore morale but next was New Zealand – a tough challenge.

Mitch had enjoyed some great performances against the Kiwis but this time had a poor game by his high standards.

He scored just one of Australia's 388 runs with the bat, didn't take a wicket and was hammered around the ground by the New Zealand batters. His figures of 0–89 were his worst at a World Cup and the first time in 24 games that he'd failed to take a wicket. On the bright side, he took three good catches in a row and Australia won . . . by just five runs in the highest-scoring

World Cup game ever. Phew!

Australia made it to the semi-finals, but Mitch copped lots of criticism, some from close to home. His uncle-in-law, Ian Healy, claimed in an interview with *SENQ Breakfast* in November 2023, "He has not been potent at all in this tournament."

Mitch knew that he and Josh Hazlewood had to make an early impact in the semi-final against South Africa. They simply had to take wickets and bowl well from the very start.

Mitch ran in hard, heart pumping, and delivered a great first over. The ball was swinging a little and just one run was scored off his first five deliveries. Mitch felt in good rhythm as he bounded in to bowl the final ball at South Africa's captain, Temba Bavuma.

The ball pitched and travelled across Bavuma who clipped the ball . . . straight into the gloves of Australia's wicketkeeper, Josh Inglis.

"Howzat!"

Umpire Joel Wilson raised his finger.
Another first over wicket for Mitch!

It got even better for Australia as Josh Hazlewood
took two wickets sandwiched between Mitch
dismissing the dangerous Aiden Markram.
South Africa were absolutely reeling at 24 for 4
and did exceptionally well to reach 212.

Mitch with 3 for 34 must have thought that
his work was over, with such a low score on
a good wicket for Australia's batters to chase.
But at 175 for 4, Mitch had to go out to bat.
Australia needed him to get them over the line.

Australia lost their seventh wicket, but
Mitch stood firm. He and Pat Cummins batted
with patience as the overs ebbed away.
Would Australia fold? Nope! Mitch crunched
a powerful four through midwicket to bring the

Aussies within two of victory. The winning runs were scored next over by Cummins. Victory! And Australia could now look forward to the final.

As Sky Sports reported in November 2023, Mitch said, "It's certainly going to be an occasion [. . .] It's going to be loud. It's going to be a great spectacle of cricket, no doubt."

Close to 100,000 spectators, mostly Indian fans, crammed into the Narendra Modi Stadium in Ahmedabad for the final. Mitch walked out with a special black armband on his right bicep. It was embroidered with the initials PH for Mitch's friend, Phillip Hughes. How he would have loved to play in this match.

Captain Pat won the toss again and asked India to bat first – a brave and risky move. India had won ten games in a row. If they got going, their formidable batting line-up could post a monster score.

India started quickly, scoring 30 in less than four overs, but then Mitch struck. He dismissed Shubman Gill in the fourth over with a ball that reared up and resulted in a comfortable catch for Adam Zampa. Rohit Sharma was next out, but India rallied with both Virat Kohli and KL Rahul scoring fifties.

Australia's bowling stayed tight and accurate, and Mitch struck again with a brilliant ball to get rid of Rahul. He finished with figures of 3 for 55. They turned out to be the best by a bowler on any side in the final.

Some Indian fans in the crowd were subdued after India's performance with the bat.

"I tell you, 240 is not enough."

"Yeah, we needed 280 or 290 at least."

"Credit to Australia, they bowled and fielded superbly."

It looked like India might turn the match

around when they wobbled Australia with three quick wickets. But a sparkling century from Travis Head saw Australia home. As Glenn Maxwell hit the winning runs, Mitch and the rest of the team sprinted out onto the field. Australia had done it – they were now six-time ODI World Cup winners!

Mitch and his teammates jumped and cheered on the winners' podium as captain Pat hoisted the heavy gold and silver trophy high above his head. A massive burst of fireworks lit up the stadium. What a scene! What a day!

The team returned to their dressing room and celebrated for quite some time. Match-winner Travis Head sat alone with the trophy deep in thought, then Glenn Maxwell danced with it round the dressing room. Mitch just enjoyed the celebrations, posing for photos with the trophy and reflecting on an amazing tournament turnaround.

⭐ CHAPTER 15 ⭐

Next Move, Mitch?

As the Australian team flew home with their World Cup winners' medals safely stored, the sports media were asking lots of questions. The player Mitch had made both his New South Wales and Australian Test debuts with, David Warner, had already announced retirement plans. Would Mitchell Starc also retire?

After all, he had won everything there is to win in the game. Along with Pat Cummins, Josh Hazlewood, Steve Smith and David Warner, Mitch is one of only five players to have been crowned World Test, World ODI and World T20i champions. He'd starred in ODIs and T20is, and done everything you can do in Test cricket . . . apart from score a pesky century!

With his efforts in India in 2023, Mitch had taken 65 World Cup wickets. This put him above his idol, Wasim Akram, and Sri Lanka's Lasith Malinga, to become the third highest World Cup wicket-taker in history. As the *Business Standard* reported in November 2023, Mitch admitted that he wouldn't be adding to his tally as he had "no vision" to play at the next World Cup in 2027.

But that didn't mean he was retiring. Far from it! In less than a month, he was back in action, in Perth, taking five wickets in a Test match against Pakistan. Following that three-match series, there were two Tests against West Indies, then a long run of ODIs. Mitch hoped to play in as many of those games as possible.

As 2023 drew to a close, Alyssa received some

amazing news. She was appointed captain of the Australian women's cricket team in all formats of the game. Mitch was thrilled for her. The following year, playing as captain against South Africa, Alyssa equalled Mitch's highest Test score as the couple became the first in Test history to both score 99 in an innings . . . and both in their ninth Test match. Spooky!

Mitch's 348 wickets in Test cricket puts him fifth on the all-time Australian list headed by super spinner, Shane Warne. Only two fast bowlers are above him: Dennis Lillee and Glenn McGrath and Lillee's total is just seven wickets away. Surely, he can do it?

He certainly hopes so. As shown in a June 2023 interview with Andy Bull in the *Guardian*, Mitch values Test cricket extremely highly: "There's nothing I love more in cricket than to sit back with my teammates at the end of a Test win and reflect on the success we've had that week. To be able to pull on the baggy green with a lot of my close mates, guys I've grown up in the game with."

Away from Test cricket, Mitch decided that it was high time he returned to the Indian Premier League and entered his name into the IPL auction on 19 December 2023, along with 332 other hopefuls. He hadn't played in the IPL since 2015 and was now a veteran, so he didn't know what to expect.

England's Harry Brook was one of the first players to be sold, for £380,000. Then, Mitch's captain, Pat Cummins, broke records as the Sunrisers Hyderabad paid 205 million Indian rupees – that's equal to about £1,935,000!

Moments later, there was yet more uproar as the Kolkata Knight Riders smashed that record. They made Mitch the most expensive player ever in the IPL by paying £2,335,000 for his services.

Next Move, Mitch?

The Knight Riders had used up more than three-quarters of their auction budget on just one player. Wow!

As ESPNcricinfo reported in December 2023, Mitch was thrilled. "They are amazing numbers, aren't they?" he said after the auction. "It's obviously humbling to still feel like I'm wanted or needed."

Whatever happens in the IPL and future ODI matches, Mitch hopes to keep putting on his old baggy green cap to take part in Test matches.

"Over a hundred years of Test cricket and there's been less than 500 men who have played it for Australia," he said in an interview with the *Guardian* in June 2023. That, in itself, makes it very special to be a part of [. . .] The traditionalist in me still hopes there is a generation of boys and girls who want to represent their country in Test cricket."

Mitchell Starc Fact File

(as of April 2024)

Born: 30/01/1990, Baulkham Hills, Australia

Tests
89 matches
2,093 runs, 358 wickets, 39 catches
0 hundreds, 10 fifties, 213 fours, 46 sixes
Bowling average: 27.74

ODIs
121 matches
571 runs, 236 wickets, 44 catches
0 hundreds, 1 fifty, 42 fours, 14 sixes
Bowling average: 22.96

T20 Internationals
60 matches
94 runs, 74 wickets, 18 catches
0 hundreds, 0 fifties, 4 fours, 2 sixes
Bowling average: 23.33

Read more sports books from Red Shed!

Amazing Cricket Stars

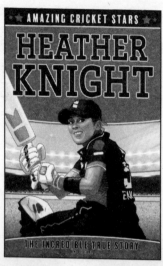

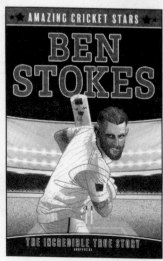

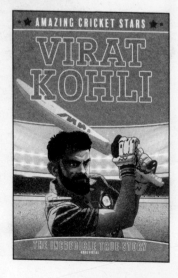

Incredible Sports Stories

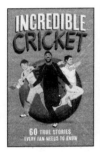   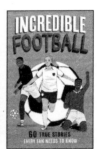

Amazing Football Facts

About the Author

CLIVE GIFFORD is an award-winning author of more than 200 books, including the official guide to the ICC Cricket World Cup 2019. His books have won the Blue Peter Children's Book Award, the Royal Society Young People's Book Prize, the School Library Association's Information Book Award and Smithsonian Museum's Notable Books For Children. Clive lives in Manchester within a short walk of Lancashire's Old Trafford cricket ground.

Read on for an extract from
Amazing Cricket Stars: Heather Knight

★ **CHAPTER 1** ★

First in all Formats

"C'mon, Trev!"

Heather 'Trev' Knight walked out onto the green sun-dappled turf at the Manuka Oval cricket ground in Canberra, Australia. A gentle breeze ruffled the flags flying on the boundary. The scenic ground was ringed by oak, elm and poplar trees. It was a lovely place to be and a glorious day for batting – but Heather was walking out into the middle of a World Cup crisis.

Three days earlier, England had suffered a bruising defeat in their opening game of the 2020 Women's T20 tournament. This competition featured the world's best women's national teams in matches lasting twenty overs a side.

England had scored 123 runs against the South
Africans and felt it was not quite enough.
Heather's contribution had been a scratchy
six runs from 14 balls before opposing captain,
Dane van Niekerk, had got her out.

In reply, van Niekerk and Marizanne Kapp took
South Africa into the nineties before both were
out and the scoring rate slowed. With three overs
to go, South Africa still needed 33 runs, but just as
Heather and her teammates thought they might
triumph, a couple of towering sixes saw the South
Africans win with only two balls left.

Heather hadn't slept well after that loss.
As captain of the team, her mind was racing.
"You can find yourself stewing after these close
games – I've already found fifteen runs we could
have saved in the field in multiple ways," she
wrote in her BBC Sport blog in February 2020.
She knew there was no need to panic but
another defeat could see England exit the
tournament early.

The Thailand team England were facing at Manuka possessed some dangerous players. Their veteran all-rounder, Nattaya Boochatham, had taken more T20 international wickets (40) in 2019 than any other player. Each wicket had cost her team just 6.17 runs. Getting past her and her leg spinning teammate, Suleeporn Laomi (who had taken 37 T20 wickets herself in 2019) was not going to be easy.

Still, as number four in a strong batting order, Heather had hoped to put her feet up and watch her team's openers, Amy Jones and Danni Wyatt, build a big partnership. There was even the buffer of the supremely talented Nat Sciver-Brunt at number three. Surely, the captain could sit back and enjoy the view?

Not a chance.

END OF SAMPLE

The Island Dog Squad
(Book 1: Sandy's Story)
By Deb McEwan

The right of Deb McEwan to be identified as the author of this work has been asserted by her in accordance with the Copyright, Designs and Patents Act 1988.

This is a work of fiction. While some places and events are a matter of fact, the characters are the product of the author's imagination and are used in a fictitious manner. Any resemblance to actual persons, living or dead, is purely coincidental.

Cover Design by Jessica Bell

For all animal lovers – you rock!

Chapter 1

I struggled to put one paw in front of the other, and was dying of thirst and hunger. Nothing was right in my world and I couldn't have gone on for much longer when they picked me up. Fit to drop, I must have let my guard down; normally I would run a mile from strangers. This one stroked me, her words soothing as she did so.

'Good boy. What have they done to you eh?'

I'm a girl actually, but I didn't have the energy to correct her with a bark.

'Come on,' she said to the man with her. 'We're taking him to the shelter.'

'But, Shel, the football, and she's a bitch actually.'

Charming. Either the look on Shel's face stopped any further words, or it could have been that I picked that exact moment to collapse in a heap on the roadside.

When I woke up I was being poked and prodded by a man in a white coat. I growled when he stuck a needle in me but was soon sleeping again.

Barking woke me the next time, lots of it. I panicked, having no idea where I was, and wondered why I felt so frightened. I was in a heavy plastic bed, which had been layered with a few old blankets. They were soft and comfortable and I took a moment to memorise their smell, just in case some other scamp tried to take them from me. Looking around, I could see I was in a concrete pen. A smallish, black dog was sleeping in a bed similar to mine, but I decided not to introduce myself until I felt more

3

comfortable with my surroundings. There was plenty of room for exercise and there was also a kennel; good protection from any bad weather, I thought. I got up, deciding to have a sniff around. I still felt very weak and had to take a moment to steady myself before moving slowly so I could explore.

The sides of the pen had large concrete walls, but the back had a wire fence I could see out of. The bottom half of my new home sloped downwards with a view of rolling green hills and the sea in the distance – not bad considering this must be a home for four-legged down-and-outs. There was also a wire fence at the front, well two actually, because in-between the fences was a concrete walkway. I looked up as I heard metal clang on metal and saw a woman carrying a bowl of food. She unlocked a gate, stepped into the walkway and locked the gate behind her. Then she opened the gate to my cage. The black dog jumped out of her bed as if a rocket had gone off, then barking manically, leapt at the woman.

I was hungry too, but didn't have the energy to compete with my roomie.

'Quiet, Scamp, there's a good girl, this one's for Sansa.'

I couldn't believe my roomie was actually called Scamp - and who the heck was Sansa?

Scamp jumped up. 'Stop it you naughty girl,' said the woman but she ignored her and kept jumping. I heard another clang and looked towards the entrance; a smaller older woman approached with a bowl of food.

'Scamp, behave.'

4

It did the trick and Scamp sighed as she plopped to the floor. Both women were now in the pen and I thumped my tail gratefully as the first one put the food down in front of me, smiled, and gave me a quick tickle behind my right ear. I loved that, but my first priority was to eat. I couldn't remember the last time I had been served food by somebody who showed me affection and smiled at me. In fact, I couldn't remember anything.

Both humans watched as I started to wolf down the biscuits. Scamp had finished hers in super-quick time and went to put her head in my bowl. Some dogs have no manners so I gave a low warning growl. I didn't want to start our relationship on the wrong paw, but then again, I was nobody's fool so had to set the boundaries. She got the message and skulked back to her bed, letting me finish my meal in peace.

'Good girl, Sansa,' the woman said as I emptied my bowl.

I risked a head nudge and it worked.

'You're going to fit in well here,' she said as she rubbed my head. It wasn't exactly what I had in mind so I rolled onto my back, lifting my legs into the air.

'You are just adorable,' she said laughing, then turned her attention to my belly giving me a wonderful tickle as I had hoped she would. I had a feeling that new people had to be trained to do what I liked. I turned my head to the side and caught Scamp rolling her eyes at me. I gave a little wink and I think I saw a slow smile. My roomie and I were going to get on just fine.

5

After the women left, Scamp came over to me with her tail so low it almost dragged on the floor.

'Hi,' she said. 'I'm Scamp and I am so sorry I tried to take your food. I've been in here on my own for a while and forgotten what it means to share. It won't happen again.'

'Apology accepted,' I said. 'I guess I'm Sansa now.'

'What's your real name?'

I didn't know so shook my head and, I was grateful she didn't push for information.

'My name's nothing like the one I had before coming here.'

'Oh?' I barked, waiting to hear more.

'My people parents named me Gladys.'

Gladys? What sort of name was that for a dog? I cocked my head to one side, trying not to laugh.

'I know,' Scamp sighed and lay down, putting her head on her paws. 'I was named after an old aunt of one of my people parents. Apparently they adored each other so that made me think my human mummy would adore me too.'

I opened my mouth to speak, surprised to hear her talk about her human mum. She understood instantly.

'That's what they become, Sansa. There's nothing better than being in a pack with family who love you and you love them. I honestly believed we were going to be together for life.'

I waited for her to tell me more but she didn't. After what seemed like an eternity I asked. 'So what happened?'

She looked pleased with my question and continued. 'They were all very loving and treated me well. The kids teased me a bit when the people parents weren't looking, but only in fun, you know, nothing cruel.'

I didn't know but gave a little nod anyway.

'Then one night it all changed. My human dad was out, and after the kids had gone to bed, I had a cuddle with mum on the sofa. It was the end of the work week. I only knew this because she had a glass of the red smelly stuff, which made her talk more than usual. She told me all about her work and what the plans were for the weekend. I nodded off, then next thing I knew, dad returned, ignored me, and they started shouting. It was scary so I rushed to my bed and watched.'

She was quiet again. After what seemed like an age I hesitantly asked, 'What happened?' I didn't like to be nosey but it was as if she expected it.

Scamp looked at me and then carried on her story. She spoke in a hushed voice and I had to strain to hear. 'He was very angry and ran up the stairs. He came back down with a bag a few minutes later and said he was leaving. By this time mum was crying, but he ignored her as he left the house and slammed the door. She kept saying, "What are we going to do, Gladys?" I couldn't answer her question so comforted her as much as I could. She picked me up and cried into my fur. After a while she cuddled me on the sofa, stroking and telling me what a good girl I was. I waggled my tail and put my head to one side to show I was listening when she talked.

I think I helped her, but I didn't know then that the writing was on the wall.'

'Looking back on those days I can see I was pretty innocent and very naive. Dad stayed away, which made mum sad. She cried when the kids were in bed, and the boys, Dylan and Oscar, occasionally cried for their father. I thought he would come back and everything would carry on as normal. It didn't. The packers arrived when the boys were in school. She told me she loved me and was sorry, then brought me here. I hadn't even been allowed to say goodbye to the boys. I'm not sure how long ago that was, but it still hurts like a knife has cut my heart in two.'

'I'm so sorry...' I said, but she had her back to me and headed back to her bed. Within seconds she was snoring softly. Poor thing. I would need to ask whether she wanted me to call her Gladys or Scamp.

I can't say I was looking forward to meeting all the other lodgers. I daresay none of them had a happy story to tell, and what about me? How would they react when I told them I couldn't remember a thing before being found wandering the streets?

Who was I and where had I come from?

Chapter 2

I soon got into the routine: up, breakfast, walk, toilet, nap, wait for the next lot of volunteers, walk, tea, sleep. It wasn't as bad as I make it sound – you can't knock free food, accommodation and lots of cuddles, even though my blankets were second-hand and I didn't have people parents to call my own. I got to know the other lodgers during the quiet times, and listened to their stories. The only happy endings were the dogs I hadn't met; those that had been picked to join families. Some poor souls had gone to their maker from the centre, never knowing what it was like to be part of a family or to be loved by caring people they could call their own. Even though I hadn't yet experienced that, after hearing Scamp's story, and the tales of some of the other dogs, I knew what I wanted; my own home and people parents who would treat me well and keep me with them forever. In return, I would give them unconditional love, loyalty and lots of fun.

When my four-legged companions asked questions about my background, I decided it was best to tell the truth. Some were sceptical in the beginning, assuming I was a bad one and that my true colours would eventually show. Attitudes changed when they got to know me. The consensus among the other lodgers was that I'd suffered some sort of trauma too awful to imagine, hence my memory loss. I did remember how tired and hungry I had been when Shel and her man found me.

As the days turned into weeks, I remained grateful for what I had, but an occasional smell or noise made me check my surroundings to ensure nobody was after me. Sometimes the sudden sounds of the hunters shouting or shooting in the distance would make me run to the safety of my bed and cower under my favourite blanket. As I lay there trembling, my heart beating wildly, I wanted to hide from the world forever. Even the deep laughter of the workmen at the rescue centre could send me into hiding. When that happened I usually received lots of love and cuddles from one of the people on duty, so it wasn't all bad. But why would laughter frighten me?

Dogs and cats came and went, but not Scamp, as she'd asked me to call her. She told me she couldn't cope with the stress of being selected then possibly rejected all over again, so, if anyone expressed interest in her, by the second or third walk she had put them off. It usually involved inappropriate pee or poo with apologies from the centre staff. After taking her for a walk and then giving her a good brush, one poor woman looked horrified when Scamp jumped onto the chair where she'd left her coat, then peed all over it. Scamp's plan worked to perfection and the woman changed her mind and adopted a relatively new lodger named Nigel, instead. Kathryn, the specialist trainer had been brought in but couldn't find anything wrong with Scamp, as she only played up when she was worried she might be leaving.

My time in the centre passed the one hundred and fifty-day mark. I resigned myself that this was to be my life

10

but also wondered if there was someone out there willing to take a chance on me.

Not much later, two people I hadn't met before took me for a walk – this wasn't unusual as the centre had a number of walker volunteers, so we were used to meeting new people.

'You are absolutely beautiful and a good girl too,' the woman said, then tickled me behind my ears and under the chin. 'This is the one,' she said to the man. He didn't reply but kissed her on the cheek.

I looked out for them during the following days and right enough, they came for me again and again. I wasn't walking at the same time as the other dogs, which made me think there was something different with these two. I knew better than to allow myself to get attached to the newbies, but still enjoyed their company, especially the man. Despite my best efforts, there was a bond between us and I looked forward to his visits. It was during the fourth walk when the woman leaned down to give me a cuddle when I discovered my future.

'You're coming home with us next Wednesday, Sandy. Oh yes you are,' she said, as she stroked the part of my back that made me tingle. It was heaven and I didn't have to force my tail to wag.

After they left, when most of the other dogs and cats were having their afternoon nap, I contemplated my future. There was no point worrying, as I didn't have a choice in the matter. Saying that, they seemed decent sorts and I'd already fallen for him, so I'd give it a go, assuming I could always come back if I didn't like it with them. I stopped that train of thought remembering the state of Foxy. She had gone to her supposedly "forever home" and had been brought back to the centre three months later. It had taken that long for her people parents to decide they couldn't trust her with the children. Foxy had a habit of play biting and they interpreted this as dangerous behaviour. I couldn't get my head around it and wondered if I would ever understand people. I also wondered about my new name. I was so glad they hadn't decided on a stupid name. I'd heard some dogs being named after places, beers or even fruits, which was very undignified. Just ask Apple!

Yes, 'Sandy' had a certain ring about it that I liked, and even the regulars at the centre said it suited me.

Wednesday soon arrived. I could feel the buzz around me as they dry shampooed and brushed me, ensuring I looked my best. I was left alone with Scamp as we enjoyed a few treats before being told I was to be picked up at one-thirty. I don't bark very often – only when absolutely necessary – but the excitement as my time approached was contagious and I barked and wagged my tail like some sort of wild dog. I was certainly high on life.

They did the paperwork, then took me outside. Scamp nuzzled my neck in a rare display of affection.

'I'm going to miss you,' she said, when she came up for air. 'As far as roomie's go you're just the best.'

Unable to hide my surprise, my eyes opened wide. Scamp chuckled. 'I don't think you know how special you are. Go on, Sandy, show them how lucky they are to have you.' She nudged my neck and then turned away.

'Hang on,' I gave a gentle bark but Scamp ignored me and kept walking. I was having none of it.

'You're pretty special too,' I shouted, then thought, what the heck. I took a run and jump and my front paws hit her side. The momentum knocked her off her feet and we rolled over and play fought for a bit. I knew it was time to go so got up and shook myself. Scamp's tail was still wagging as we said our final goodbyes.

'Good luck for the future, Scamp. I hope you change your mind and find your...'

'Don't say it,' she said. 'Now go on, off you go.'

Despite how she felt, I really hoped she would find her forever home. If anyone deserved love and kindness it was good old Scamp. Now I put her out of my mind and concentrated on the new people.

'Let's go home, Sandy,' the female said as we walked towards their car.

People think that dogs don't get embarrassed, but they are absolutely wrong. I so wanted to create a good first impression but was shaking too much to attempt a leap into the back of the car.

'It's too high for her,' the man said kindly. 'Come on girl.' Before I knew what he had in mind he'd lifted me onto the seat. My imagination started running riot. What if these people weren't taking me to their home and they were the sorts who destroyed dogs? What if it was all one big con and there was no such thing as a forever home? What if the centre couldn't afford to feed me anymore and I had to be...

'It's okay, Sandy. Everything's going to be all right.' The woman's words helped a little. My heart stopped racing but I could still feel myself shaking; it was all very scary.

'Look at her, Ben, poor thing's shaking.'

Ben turned around for a brief look before returning his attention to the road. 'We'll soon have you home and settled, Sandy, don't you worry, girl.'

Despite my distress I memorised his name, then got to wondering. Could this really be it? I remained on high alert just in case it was one big wind-up.

I'm not sure how much later it was when he stopped the car. She got out and closed some gates, while he picked me up and put me on the ground. I had a little sniff around, then looked at my surroundings: big garden, few plants and mostly concreted areas. That was going to be hot in the summer.

'Come on, girl,' he said, 'let's show you your new home.'

Oh, all right then. I was still on the lead so had no choice but to follow.

'That's where you're going to live with us,' the woman said, as she nodded to the big house. 'And in the summer when it gets really hot, we've got a big surprise for you.'

It was funny because they talked to me as if I were a child, explaining each area of the garden.

There were lots of interesting smells, but mostly of cats; feral mixed with tame. Now, I wasn't one for chasing and barking at them like I'd seen some dogs do - in fact, Scamp went mental every time she passed one of the cats at their own part of the centre. I found them more confusing than people, and the ones I'd tried to get along with been quite stuck-up, but as long as they didn't bother me, I was happy to leave them alone.

I could scent the dog over the fence and I looked in that direction as I heard barking, then growling. This wasn't a happy chap. I went to approach to say hello but Ben pulled me back.

'That's a mad dog, Sandy, ignore it.'

I did as bid and the tour continued.

In the middle of all the stonework was a beautiful, blue, water feature. Ah, this must be the surprise. I thought I'd won the jackpot! From starving dog wandering the streets, to rescue centre, to home with a pool. I was looking forward to cooling off in there during the hot summer months.

Inside wasn't too shabby either. The wooden floors were a little loud when I walked around but I would soon get used to that. There was a comfortable looking bed containing a blanket and a few items of human clothing, which made me wonder if I was sharing the house with another animal. I couldn't smell any and was confused, wondering where I would sleep later.

'I'll get her stuff, Ellie.'

I memorised her name too and stood awkwardly, waiting for something to happen.

'I'll show you around inside, Sandy,' Ellie said, so I followed her as she explained where I was to eat, drink and relax. 'This is your bed, Sandy, come on, girl, jump in.' It wasn't bedtime but I had a tentative sniff. The soft human clothes smelled of Ben and Ellie, but the other scents I didn't recognise. I wasn't sure about it and had no intention of trying it out. To be honest it was all getting a bit too much.

'Come on, Sandy, you'll love it.' She grabbed my collar, trying to drag me into the bed. So what was wrong with it if she had to force me to use it? Feeling a little nervous I stood my ground, but it was a struggle. I needed a wee so could have done without the hassle.

Ben returned and took in the scene. 'Her tail's down, Ellie. Perhaps it's too much, too soon. Let's go and sit in the garden and let her have a proper sniff around. Get used to her new surroundings.'

Good idea Ben. This man was one switched-on cookie. I had hoped to go for a walk later and would find a suitable place to do my business, but unfortunately couldn't wait. They had a few trees and a small green area so I went there. Oh the relief!

'Good girl, Sandy,' said Ellie, while clapping her hands as if I'd done a somersault. So this was important. Thank goodness I'd held it in, in the house. I now knew I would have ruined my chances of staying if I'd had to go inside. Sad to say, my relief was short lived.

We all went for a walk, then they put food down for me. After we all relaxed for a while, they started to make a move.

'Good night, Sandy, sleep well.' Ellie said. She stroked me, then disappeared up the steps. Ben followed a few minutes later.

Ben had put the blanket I used at the centre into the new bed. I still didn't have the confidence to go in it, but they'd also said goodnight without telling me to go to bed, so what was I supposed to do? I lay on the floor for a while. It was comfortable enough but I struggled to sleep, trying to get used to all the strange noises. I eventually nodded off but wasn't sure whether a noise or my stomach woke me up. The people were nowhere to be seen and I didn't know what to do. I was busting and the inevitable happened. The best I could do was to go on the rug. I was mortified. To reflect the noises coming from my stomach, suffice to say it wasn't joined up. I felt better instantly and it didn't take long to forget about my little accident and go to sleep.

The noises from upstairs woke me and it was light when I opened my eyes. I was so glad to see Ben, not only because I was hungry.

'Hello, Sandy, did you sleep well?' he asked, as he gave me a quick cuddle, but his mood quickly changed.

'Oh no, what's that stink?' He headed for the rug, looked at the mess, then at me. 'Bad girl, bad, bad girl.'

His words didn't stop there and I wondered why he was shouting at me. After all, it seemed like ages ago since I'd gone to the toilet on the rug, and I couldn't help it. Being in Ben's bad books on the first morning in my new home wasn't a good feeling. I was frightened and slunk away to the furthest corner, hoping he would stop calling me names. Ellie came to my rescue.

'Oh the poor girl. She must have been so anxious she couldn't help herself, and now all you're doing is frightening her. We need to calm her down, Ben, in case she has any more accidents.'

Actually, I did need a wee.

'Never mind calm her down, we need to clean up this mess.'

'I'll do it,' said Ellie.

By this stage Ben looked like he was starting to calm down. He approached me but I couldn't be absolutely certain. Shaking, I made myself as small as I could, just in case.

'I'm sorry, girl,' he said as he stroked me. 'I know it must have been scary for you, but don't make a habit of it, eh?' He tickled me behind the ear, so I decided to forgive him. 'Now let's go into the garden and get rid of this, then I can show you where to do your business.'

This would be interesting as I hadn't been able to find anywhere suitable during my first sniff the day before. I followed Ben to one of the smaller areas of the garden, near two trees, one laden with lemons, the other, mandoras. The surround was covered in small white pebbles that felt rough on my pads. I wasn't keen on doing my business there but took the hint; they didn't want a mess on the rug and I would do my utmost to please them. Even though it was all new to me, I was starting to like Ellie almost as much as Ben and the lifestyle they had to offer, so it was the least I could do to repay their wonderful hospitality.

I settled in and started to get used to my new surroundings. Every day brought a new experience or a new area to discover. They replaced some of the pebbles with green pretend grass which was much more comfortable, and looked better in my opinion.

'Better place for you to do your business,' Ben told me, but most of the time I did it outside the boundaries of the house, after all, I had plenty of walks every day. Sometimes I was tired, but walks are like food to us dogs. As far as I'm aware, none of us has ever turned down the opportunity to go out on the hunt, meet other dogs or people, but most importantly, have a good sniff around.

Meals were an interesting time too. I generally ate biscuits but was given snacks in between my morning or evening meal, or as encouragement when they wanted me to do something new. Well, new to Ben and Ellie, but tricks seemed to come easily to me and I was very chuffed to hear them tell friends, and even strangers, how clever I was.

Their food always looked more interesting than mine. One day Ellie had a bowl with red items, covered in white liquid. I licked my lips and tried my most pathetic doe-eyed look.

'Ah, look at her, Ben.'

I was in with a chance then.

'Mummy's a fruitivore, Sandy,' said Ben, 'and you're a carnivore, so you won't like strawberries.'

'But she eats biscuits too,' said Ellie. 'Surely we can give her some of our food now and then?'

Hey guys, remember me? I nudged Ben's leg, but he ignored me.

'It'll make her think she can come to the table and scrounge and neither of us want that.'

'True,' said Ellie. 'Go lie down, Sandy.'

I sighed and went to sulk in my bed. I had nothing to complain about but, like I said earlier, their food always looked more appealing than mine. I was to discover that Ellie was also a vegivore and chocivore. Strangely enough, she was also a carnivore and so was Ben. As a special treat one weekend, I was given some roast pork, and it was heaven.

Shortly after, I heard them talking about returning to work, which was a new one on me. The next morning when we got up they were all business. A quick stroke as Ellie enquired how I'd slept, 'fine thank you.' Then Ben put his trainers on and told me it was time to go out. I still had sleep in my eyes so this was a surprise. He didn't allow me to stop and sniff as much as usual and when I'd done my business, we headed back home. Ellie had my breakfast ready, and while I ate, Ben went up for a quick shower. I stopped eating and turned to Ellie. By now, we were all tuned into each other so she knew I was curious.

'We've been on holiday, Sandy, to get you settled in. We have to go back to work today, so we can pay the bills and buy food. We'll soon get into a routine and your long walks will be at the weekend.'

Oh, okay. I turned back to my food, not completely sure what all of this meant. I heard Ben coming down the stairs and went to greet him. He gave me a quick pat and so did Ellie.

'Bye, Sandy, see you later,' Ben said to me. 'Don't make too much of a fuss,' he said to Ellie, 'we don't want her to have separation anxiety.'

'Yes, Ben,' Ellie replied. I saw her roll her eyes but I don't think he noticed.

I looked out of the patio doors as both cars disappeared down the driveway. They'd left the radio on for me, which I thought considerate. How did they know I enjoyed music?

It was the first time I'd been on my own during the day in ages. I played with some toys, knowing that I could keep myself amused, but given the choice, I did prefer company.

You have to be careful what you wish for at times – a cat appeared at the patio door and walked up and down with her tail in the air. I guess the dog next door could smell it, or it might have been something else that caught its attention, because it started barking. It didn't take much to start him barking to be honest. We hadn't met yet, although I had tried to introduce myself. When I was sniffing around the garden one day, I went to the fence to say hello - he went ballistic and it was a shock to my senses. Ben and Ellie wouldn't let me stay to talk to him so I hadn't had the chance to find out why he was so unhinged.

The cat walked by again. I'm sure she was trying to wind me up. I'm generally quite laid back and happy to share, but I hate bad manners. She hadn't even asked if she could use our garden so I had to put her right.

I walked around the downstairs area, looking at each door and window. Keys were in the front and back doors – difficult, but not impossible for me – and a few of the smaller windows were tilted open. I was too big to get through these so I came back to the patio door. The handle was down meaning it was locked from the inside. I already knew how it opened and closed having seen Ben and Ellie operate it many times. I jumped up. My front paws reached the bottom of the handle, but I couldn't get the purchase to turn it. Back on four legs I strolled around for a bit, thinking. It seemed I enjoyed problem solving but something told me it had been a while since I'd had to.

Then I looked at the dining area. Easy, peasy! Why had it taken me so long to work it out?

The chair was manageable so I put my teeth gently around one of the legs, so as not to leave any lasting marks, and dragged it to the patio door. When it was close enough I jumped up onto it. I didn't need to stand on my back paws to reach the handle now, so sat close to it and, using both front paws, pulled it. I nearly fell off the chair when the handle moved, unlocking the door. I pulled it open so there was just enough room for me to get through, then opened the fly screen. I walked outside, shutting the fly screen behind me - Ellie was prone to insect bites so I didn't want to be responsible for letting any into the house. The cat looked at me as if she'd seen a ghost.

'Get out of my garden,' I barked in a tone that brooked no argument. She'd regained her composure by this stage and decided to push her luck, as cats sometimes do. Giving me a dirty look she sat down and started cleaning her nether regions. I growled and approached her, trying to look as scary as possible. It must have done the trick as she did a runner. On the other side of the gate she made some hissing noises. Brave, eh?

'Yeah, yeah, whatever,' I said. 'Next time you want to come into my garden, have the decency to ask first.'

As expected, she sauntered off with her tail in the air. I hoped there wouldn't be a next time with this one. Now for the dog next door – but this wasn't going to be so easy.

'If you come any nearer, I'm... I'm going to hurt you,' he barked at me, 'this time I will kill you.' The threat didn't match the voice, which was shaky and unsure. This wasn't the first time he'd threatened me, and he sounded frightened. Knowing that fear makes dogs unpredictable, I approached with caution.

'Look, pal, we're neighbours so we might as well try to get along.' My tail was up and wagging gently as I tried to put him at ease.

'Don't hurt me,' he barked back, and the tooing and froing from threat to pleading set the tone for the conversation.

'I don't want to hurt you,' I said patiently, 'what's your name?'

Ignoring my question, he had another go.

'That's my fence, keep away.' Now he growled, showing his teeth menacingly.

I took a step back, trying to demonstrate that I wasn't a threat. 'Perhaps we can go on walks together?' I suggested, but it was no good. As he continued to bark empty threats followed by pleas for me not to hurt him, he started to bang his head on the fence, over and over. I made one last ditch attempt, in the hope he would stop the head banging at the very least. 'If you change your mind, give me a shout,' I said.

My words fell on deaf ears.

As I headed back to the house I had a sneaky look and noticed the head banging had stopped. That was a relief. The cat that was in my garden earlier was now next door, along with a partner in crime. They were sitting on the shed roof, tormenting my neighbour just by their presence. It was sad that he was too traumatised to tell me his story, but I knew he must have been through something horrendous to end up like this. He was what we in the dog world knew as a no-hoper, and his human family had made the situation worse by leaving him outside while they were out of the home all day. At least I had the comfort and security of the house, not to forget the company of my radio.

I decided not to wander around the neighbourhood today, so returned to the house, locking the patio door behind me and returning the chair to the table.

It didn't occur to me that other dogs lacked the skills and talents that I had.

I was excited when my people parents returned home later and greeted them as if I hadn't seen them for years. All was well in my world. I was madly in love with Ben and Ellie, missed the guys at the centre less and less, and wanted for nothing. I did still wonder about my past, but less often than I used to.

Then I met Lola and everything changed.

Chapter 3

I heard the key in the door. Knowing it was one of Ben's golf days I expected to see Ellie. I wasn't disappointed and dived at her. After all, it felt like a lifetime since I'd last seen her.

'Hello, Sandy. I love you too,' she said, laughing as she bent to give me lots of love and cuddles. They both did this after being out, which I believe was their way of apologising for leaving me to my own devices for so long. Ellie had a part-time job so I wasn't on my own all day like some dogs. As well as leaving the radio on they always left me plenty of water and put some treats in what they considered to be a complex toy, expecting me to take a while to work out how to remove them. They were kind and very thoughtful people parents. I loved them and they felt the same about me, so we were all grateful to have found each other.

'We're going for a walk with Auntie Gina and you're going to meet your new friends Lola and Obie. Your Auntie Gina is one of my besties and I hope you get along with Obie as well as I do with Gina, without the wine of course.'

Ellie chuckled but it must have been a people thing and I missed the joke, just as they sometimes didn't get my dog stuff. Like when I had a funny half hour and kept jumping onto the settee uninvited, crouching, then jumping off and running around like a looney. Fun was fun and sometimes it just had to be done.

'...Not so much with Lola as she's not as lively. In fact, she's never been a lover of long walks.' Ellie laughed and I gave her a strange look. What sort of dog didn't like long walks for goodness sake?

'I know, Sandy. She is a bit weird.'

Fair enough, it takes all sorts. She put my lead on and I didn't resist the excitement. My tail went into automatic hyperactive propeller mode. Off we went with me trying to bring my overactive wagger under control.

I knew Ben and Ellie weren't my real parents and their friends weren't my aunties or uncles, but if it made them happy, I would gladly play along.

My new Auntie Gina and her pack lived a ten-minute walk away. As we made our way there, Ellie explained that Auntie Gina was a businesswoman, so her working routine depended on the number of clients she had on any given day. I struggled to pay attention as I sniffed the new area, and followed a few of the interesting scents. I think Ellie was used to this. She always talked to me while we were on our own and wasn't bothered when I ignored her while we were out. Saying that, she did expect me to pay attention to her one or two word orders, so I did and we were both happy. All of a sudden I realised that Ellie was talking and I hadn't been paying attention.

'Come, Sandy,' she said, and I could tell by her tone of voice that it wasn't the first time she'd told me. I stopped sniffing the bush and bounded over to her.

'Sit.' I did as bid then gave a lopsided grin. 'Good girl, Sandy,' she said, and then patted my head. 'What took you so long?'

Was there any need for that sarcasm? I wondered as we carried on to our destination. I had discovered early on that if I sat on command, spun around, gave a paw when asked and learnt other so-called tricks, it gave them both lots of pleasure. Happy people parents equalled happy dog, and it didn't take much effort on my part.

Ellie now started talking about Auntie Gina's dogs.

'So Obie's a rescue dog just like you. Don't say I said but he's not as clever. He has a very weird bark too. It's like he puts a few ee's on the end so it sounds to me like woof-ee.'

All dogs had individual barks but this did sound unusual. I decided to reserve judgement until I heard it. Ellie continued.

'He was much harder to train than you are, Sandy and can still be like a hyperactive five-year-old. He nearly drove your Auntie Gina nuts when she first brought him home. I bet you're wondering why?'

Funnily enough I was, so gave her my best "please continue" look.

Ellie laughed again. 'I'm sure you understand exactly what I'm saying. Your dad thinks I'm off my rocker when I tell him that.'

Now for my, "Well done, Sherlock" look, but it was wasted on her.

'Anyway, Gina told me he had an annoying habit of digging holes anywhere he could, but was a lot better now he'd learned to control it. Apparently it was all down to the anxiety of living in a centre and the move to Gina's. Poor

Obie, eh? As for Lola, well, between you and I, she can come across as a bit stuck up at times, and Gina said she's very stubborn. Apparently most Pugs are like that. She has a funny little habit of tapping her left paw. I've never seen a dog do that before, Sandy.'

Something started to nag at my memory, but just then a little lizard scooted by and caught my attention. I reached out a paw but missed by a mile. I looked up.

'Sorry, Ellie, what were you saying?'

'It's like they were meant to be together. Poor Gina had a puppy pug but it died unexpectedly. She was absolutely heartbroken, then a week later, Lola turned up in her garden, from out of nowhere. Gina asked around and shared her photo on Social Media but nobody came forward. She also went to the police and local authorities who said if nobody claimed her within two months she could keep her.'

'So what about Obie?'

I put my head to one side again to make Ellie laugh and it worked. 'Well Gina's son asked if he could have a dog more active than Lola, so when the two month period was up and she knew they were keeping her, they went to Pretty Paws Rescue Centre, that one up there.' Ellie pointed to a group of buildings on a hillside in the distance. 'Anyway, Gina wanted to make sure that Lola got on with any new family member, so they took her with them. Lola wasn't keen on a number of the dogs there, but as soon as she met Obie they clicked. Greg fell in love with him too so they brought him home. Her daughter Laura has always preferred cats so they've got two cats as well. Here we are then,' she said.

Ellie opened the gate and there was pandemonium. Two dogs ran round the corner from the back of the house, although I use the word ran in its loosest term. The pug waddled and the younger dog galloped and barked a scream when he recognised me. Ellie was exactly right, there was a weird ee sound at the end of his bark, but also a nervous laugh. Imagine a hyperactive child had drunk two cans of energy drinks, well this was the four-legged version. Lola the pug continued waddling in my direction looking both smug and superior.

'Sandy, meet Lola and Obie.' Ellie made the introductions.

'We've already met,' I barked, but Ellie didn't quite get it.

Obie screamed another bark. He was very excited to see me.

'I haven't heard him get so excited.'

I looked to the direction of the voice. A woman shorter than Ellie with pretty green eyes and a mass of curly red hair bent down and stroked me. 'Hello, Sandy.'

Wagging my tail enthusiastically, I nudged her hand with my head, wanting to make a good first impression.

'And this is your Auntie Gina,' said Ellie.

Gina looked up to Ellie while still cuddling me. 'She's lovely, Ellie. Such a sweet nature.'

'I know. We've struck lucky there.'

They chatted for a minute then Auntie Gina went back in her house to retrieve the snacks she'd forgotten, and the leads for the dogs. As I wracked my brains, trying to remember where I had met Lola and Obie before, Lola sidled up to me. She had a good sniff so Ellie wouldn't suspect anything then whispered. 'What oh, Fish, marvellous to see you. Don't think about it now, it'll all come back in good time. Enjoy the walk and we'll chat later.' Her refined tones rang a bell somewhere in the back of my mind, but for now I was too gobsmacked to think about anything else but what she'd called me.

'Fish? Who the heck...?'

Lola cut me off. 'That's what we call you. All will become clear. Now hurry along, we don't want them asking questions so you have to pretend we've just met. Got it? I've briefed Digger,' she could see I was confused, so quickly explained. 'Digger is the name you know Obie by. He's terribly excited but knows the score, so won't give the game away.'

Auntie Gina came out of the house and attached their leads.

'Come on, you two. At the double,' Lola ordered me and Obie, Digger, or whatever I was meant to call him.

'Aw look,' said Gina. 'Lola's in charge already, and they're following her. She can be a bossy mare.'

Both women laughed and I did wonder why I had followed her order without question.

Most of the time I try to live in the present. I enjoyed the walk with my not-so-new friends, but there were too many questions to be answered for me to let myself go completely. I heard snatches of Ellie and Gina's conversation.

31

'She seems a bit unsure, I hope they get used to each other and become friends.'

'I'm sure they will,' said Gina. 'You have to give her time, Ellie. Nobody knows what she went through before being delivered to the rescue centre, so certain smells or sights might bring back memories and freak her out.'

'Seriously? I thought dogs were meant to live in the present and forget their past.'

'I suppose to a certain degree, but if that was the case would she recognise you and Ben when you come home from work every day? You've seen how Obie freaks out when he sees Rottweilers or Dobermans. I reckon he must have had a bad experience with these dogs at some stage.'

Ellie looked thoughtful. 'I suppose you're right. Perhaps we're expecting too much too soon.'

The women carried on walking in companionable silence, watching us three as we explored the countryside. Obie ran off. Despite having a lot on my mind, I chased as far as my lead would allow, hoping they would notice I was making an effort - I was trying my best and sometimes people simply didn't realise how hard it was to please them. Saying that, it wasn't long before I got caught up in the moment and managed to park my concerns for the time being. We were soon jumping around, sniffing each other and sharing interesting smells amongst the greenery. Obie put his head on my flank, then gave me a friendly nudge. I returned the favour.

'Aw, look at them,' said Ellie. 'They are going to be best friends. We're so lucky, Gina. She's a wonderful dog with a lovely nature, and clever too. We've fallen on our feet here and even though we've had her less than two weeks, I can't imagine life without her.'

So this was to be my forever home and my people parents adored me. I felt two feet taller and headed towards Ellie with my tail wagging manically.

'I'm sure she understands what I'm saying,' Ellie laughed, and Lola intercepted me.

'Play with Obie,' she demanded, reverting back to his current name.

We cavorted until we were both worn out. As we slowed our pace, Lola approached, out of Gina and Ellie's sight.

'That's enough for today, chaps, I don't want them to see you already know each other.'

'But I don't remember Obie, or Digger, or whatever you call him. He's...'

'You will remember, Fish, all in good time. Now act tired, there's a good girl, it's time to go home. I'll come for a natter later in the week when your people are out. Don't worry, old thing, you're safe here.'

Yet again the breeding came through in her voice and somewhere in the back of my mind was a memory of listening to her and knowing I'd carry out her instructions. I put it to one side because I was absolutely shattered and didn't have to act tired. The last comment seemed a peculiar thing for Lola to say. I watched as Digger followed her instructions too. The humans noticed we were worn out, so Gina and Ellie decided it was time to go home.

Chapter 4

Ben was pulling up in his car by the time we reached home, so I jumped up at him. Now I knew how he felt about me, I decided to give him some special attention.

'Stop, Sandy, don't jump.'

Charming. I wish I hadn't bothered. I put my tail down and, sulking, made my way into the house.

'Come on, Sandy, give us a cuddle.'

Deciding to forgive his little outburst, I wagged my tail and enjoyed some one-on-one time with Ben. He took his shoes off, loosened his tie, and told me all about his day, while stroking me gently. That was better. Unfortunately, he didn't get along with his pack leader in work so was full of stress. I did my best to pay attention, which seemed to help him unwind. After we'd played for a while the tension in his body had disappeared, along with the frown lines on his face. I went to lie down as he chatted to Ellie.

'Fancy going out tonight?' he asked.

'What about Sandy?'

I closed my eyes, pretending to be asleep.

'She's used to spending time on her own during the day, love, so I'm sure she'll be fine.'

Decision made, we all had our tea then they disappeared, to the tavern I presumed. I usually preferred to have my people parents with me. They were now part of my pack and I wasn't totally comfortable when they weren't around. Tonight was different. I needed time to think about what Lola had said, and as the front door closed, it was the first time that day I had a chance to reflect on things. I was mentally and physically exhausted so instead of using the quiet time to think, my body decided to rest and it wasn't long before I was asleep.

I guess a bad dream woke me as I heard barking and it took a nano-second before I realised it was my own. I'm not one of those dogs who barks constantly, in fact I hardly bark at all. I didn't recall the dream. Shaking myself awake, I stretched, walked to my bowl and took a deep drink of water. I'd left a few biscuits in my food bowl after dinner so I wolfed those down, took another drink, then returned to the living room. I ignored my bed and lay on the floor with one of my paws folded underneath me.

The first flashback came - and it hit like a bolt of lightening. I remembered being a puppy, I'm not sure how old, on a boat with the rest of the litter and our mother. She was a beautiful black Labrador. All my siblings were black but none of us were pure Lab. She told us our father was a Collie/Husky cross. I was singled out for attention because of my blonde colour.

'Hello, Blondie,' I remembered the kindly man saying to me as he picked me up for cuddles. I loved snuggling in to his warm body and falling asleep in his arms. A young girl with long blonde hair was allowed to play with me too, but only when her father let her. She told me she loved me the best.

Then there was the woman.

Just thinking about her made my skin crawl and my body shake. In the human world she was considered beautiful beyond measure; dark skin, eyes and hair, and a body with curves in all the right places. The man displayed her as he did his other precious belongings, but didn't show her the affection he showed to me or the child. She spoke sweetly to us all when he was with her, but displayed her true spirit when she was alone with us. She singled me out for her special treatment, pulling at my tail or hitting me.

'Think you're cute do you, you blonde madam?' she would say before flicking my nose with a finger or giving me a vicious slap. I tried to avoid her but couldn't as she always grabbed me, despite my attempts to run away and hide. When my mother started to defend me, she received a punch in the side and was locked in her cage every time the woman came to visit us.

I closed my eyes trying to block out the memories of those days: the love and comfort of the master; the fun with the child; and the cruelty of the mistress who wouldn't go away, and it was as if the floodgates had opened. I reminded myself that I was now in my forever home with permanent people parents who loved and wanted me. Thinking about Ben and Ellie made me smile and I now felt better prepared to face my past.

Feeling calmer, I allowed the memories to return... It was night-time and we were all sleeping until she came to our quarters. We knew who it was by her distinctive smell. I kept my eyes closed and made myself as small as I could, in the futile hope that she would ignore me. She seemed to be bumping into things and I risked a look. She was swaying from side to side as she approached our home. My mother barked and growled from her pen, knowing something awful was going to happen, but we were below decks so nobody heard.

The mistress shoved her hand in our bed. Everyone was awake now, looking at her with fear in their eyes. But still, my brothers and sisters squeezed themselves around me, knowing that it was me she was after. As one puppy was picked up and thrown to another area of the pen, so another took its place. I was so proud of my brave siblings. Those that weren't knocked out by the impact of their landing ran back to us and attacked her with gusto. She kicked or threw them off, cursing as she did so.

'Damn dogs!' she screamed as she yanked me from my puppy sandwich and grabbed me up. Her voice was slurred and her gait unsteady. She made her way to the door, having to drag one leg behind her, trying to shake off two puppies as she did so. Those that were able were barking loudly, along with my mother. It was deafening and despite where we were on the boat, I wondered why nobody came. The mistress held me with one hand as she opened the door. I could see my brother and sister were exhausted and she managed to shake them off. The door slammed shut behind us.

After the noise of the pen, the complete silence came as a shock to my system; I was no longer surprised that nobody had heard us barking and her screaming. She held me in front of her at arms distance. The skin underneath her eyes was black. I risked a quick look into her dark orbs, hoping to see a hint of kindness, but all I noticed before

37

looking away was rage. The red paint she wore on her lips had spread to one of her cheeks. I was shaking uncontrollably by this stage, fearing the worst. She smelled the same as the master did when he walked unsteadily or laughed like a child, but he was always happy when he smelled like this. Not so the mistress.

'This is it, puppy,' she said. 'The final time I have to be reminded. You and the two-legged blonde bit are dead to me, and to him.'

I had no idea what she was talking about and it was the least of my concerns as I felt myself flying through the air. I landed with a splash. It was a shock to the system even though it was the height of summer and the water wasn't bitterly cold - but it wasn't exactly warm either. With no idea what to do, and before I could move, I felt myself go under. I started paddling like mad and managed to get my head above the water. I could breathe again. As soon as I stopped paddling I went back under. Paddling furiously again I broke the surface. I took a deep breath and this time kept at it, terrified of the consequences if I stopped. I was young and innocent, but not entirely stupid. I could feel my strength ebbing away and, despite my hard work, I was starting to get cold as well. I kept going for as long as I could, having no idea how much time had passed. As I went under again, I knew I didn't have the energy to do anything about it. Before closing my eyes for the last time I saw a large grey shape approach. It opened its mouth and I stared at teeth the size of which I could never have imagined. Another grey shape forced it out of the way and headed straight for me. This one had friendly eyes and a smiley face. At least I'd seen a pretty water creature before dying, I thought. I heard a clicking noise before losing consciousness.

Back in the present I got up and stretched. So, obviously I'd survived, but there was still a big gap in my past. I had no idea how long my people parents had been gone. I stretched again, then shook my legs. Needing a bit of exercise, I grabbed my big cushion from the computer room, snarled at it and lay into it with my teeth. When I'd had enough of that I took my blankets and toys out of my bed. I jumped on the squeaky hamburger a few times then bit into it. I could have fun on my own and the squeaky noise amused me. After a while I looked at the mess around me. I'd done this before and Ben and Ellie hadn't seemed to mind. Still, just because they'd decided to adopt me, that didn't mean I could take them for granted. I put most of my belongings back in my bed, but left the cushion where it was. I decided to lie in my bed and have a nap but couldn't get off to sleep. Now that I had discovered some of my past, I was eager to know the rest. As much as I concentrated and willed something to pop into my head, nothing happened. How did I get from losing consciousness in the big water, to a starving down-and-out dog, wandering the streets for reasons unknown to her? I sighed and bit into the hamburger toy, swinging my head from side to side, and growling with frustration.

As soon as I stopped thinking about it, images started to appear. I could see myself as a young puppy and could almost feel the heat of the sun as if I were back on that beach.

I opened my eyes and tried to move but was exhausted. I felt an overpowering desire for water, but my legs wouldn't move even though I told them to. Every time I tried to stand I collapsed back into a heap on the sand. So the sea or the big fish hadn't claimed my life, but I might now die of thirst or burn in the heat of the sun. I closed my eyes again to await my fate.

'There he is,' I heard somebody shout, and opened my eyes for a look. Two men were heading directly towards me, dressed in unusual clothes that seemed to match the sand.

'Oh, you poor boy,' said the taller of the two. He took a bottle out of the bag on his back and nodded to his companion. Without being told, his companion bent towards me and held his hands together. Water was poured into them and he offered it to me. Lots dripped onto the sand but I managed to get a decent drink.

'Hang on, Andy,' said the man who had held out his hands. He dried them on his trousers then took the beret off his head. The taller man poured the water into the beret and laid it on the sand for me. I drank to my heart's content, stood up and managed a thank you tail wag. I wasn't as strong as I thought though and soon sank back to the sand. When I'd drunk my fill, the one called Andy picked me up and gave me a cuddle. I felt safe so closed my eyes again. They started walking along the beach and I listened as they chatted.

'So you're telling me you saw a dolphin pushing something towards the shore and we get here to find him?'

'Her,' Andy corrected. 'And yes, that's exactly what I'm telling you.'

'Pull the other one, mate, it's got bells on.'

I had no idea what had bells on but was happy just to be alive and safe at that stage. All I needed now was food and somewhere comfortable to sleep and I could get by. I tried not to think about my mother and siblings, not knowing if I'd see any of them ever again.

Andy laughed, 'I would struggle to believe it too, but that's how it is.'

The other man shook his head but changed the subject. 'Let's take her to the section and see what the boss thinks. We might be able to do something with her.'

So that's how I ended up in a dog section on a military base where I was to meet Digger. Did Lola work there? She didn't look like the type of dog likely to be selected for military duties, but it took all sorts and I could be wrong.

Back in the present, I didn't have time to ponder further as I heard the key in the door. Ben staggered in first, followed by Ellie who was steadier on her feet. I wagged my tail with glee, making the back half of my body move. Ben laughed and leaned down to put his arms around me, then lost his footing. He landed on the floor on his back. They were both giggling by this stage so I jumped on him and started licking his face. The next thing I knew, Ellie was on the floor with us. They started tickling each other and me, while laughing like lunatics. I hadn't had so much fun in ages and it was good to have my mind taken off the trauma of my past. There was time to think about what happened next another day.

We were all exhausted after a while. Ellie got up and told Ben it was bedtime, but he was already sleeping, and snored loudly as he turned over onto his side. Despite her best efforts, she was unable to move him. She kissed him gently and wished him goodnight.

'Go to bed, Sandy,' she said, but I gave her a pleading look and snuggled into Ben. It was the first time I'd disobeyed her but I hoped she'd understand. She was my second favourite person but there was no way I was leaving the warmth and comfort of my favourite person to go to my bed, unless she physically forced me to. Even then, I'd be able to sneak back to Ben when Ellie was upstairs.

'Oh, okay then,' she said. 'I suppose you can keep each other warm, but I'll get you a blanket, just in case.'

She disappeared for a minute, then returned with a blanket and covered both of us. I'd pull that off during the night. Did she think my fur was for show or something?

'Goodnight, you two,' she said before kissing Ben again and then kissing me on my head. 'I love you guys.'

Aw, how sweet was that? I felt a little guilty for the unkind thought about my fur. I love you too, Ellie, nighty night, I said to myself as I licked her hand. I think she got the message. I was in doggie heaven and the strength of my feelings were such that it started to dawn on me how much they both meant to me.

It was the weekend and as Ellie opened the curtains, Ben opened his eyes.

'Ew, you have dog breath.' A bit obvious, I thought but wagged my tail and licked his face to say good morning. He gave me a pat but I could see his heart wasn't in it. His face turned very pale as he stood up and rushed to the bathroom. I listened to the unpleasant noises coming from the room, undecided whether I should check on him. When I made up my mind I pushed the door and Ben was leaning over the porcelain, retching into it. He must have heard me because he turned around and told me to go away in no uncertain terms. I thought this very rude after spending the night together. How come they were allowed to watch me use the outside toilet when we were out walking, but I wasn't allowed to watch either of them? It was one of the many mysteries of my life, but I didn't dwell on it. I needed a cuddle, so went to Ellie and she made up for Ben's rejection by giving me the attention I felt I deserved.

'He's hungover, Sandy. Serves him right for drinking too much last night.' As she continued to stroke me she whispered. 'Don't tell your dad but I'm not feeling my best today either.'

I was still in a huff with Ben so had no intention of telling him anything.

He dragged himself out of the bathroom looking marginally better. 'Sorry, pal,' he said as he attempted to stroke me. 'I didn't mean to shout and swear at you.' I remained aloof and cuddled into Ellie, keen for Ben to know where my allegiance was.

'I think you've upset her,' said Ellie.

'She's a dog and shouldn't have been in the bathroom.'

I gave a sigh and lay at Ellie's feet.

'But I did say sorry,' Ben added, before yawning. 'I'm poorly, Ellie.'

'Oh, diddums. Is Benny Wellie illy willy?' Ellie asked.

'I'm off for a lie down.'

'So I suppose I have to do the shopping on my own then?' Ellie's voice was now back to normal but Ben ignored her question as he walked upstairs and closed the bedroom door. She gave me my breakfast, let me out to do my business then got her things together to go to the supermarket.

'See you later, Sandy, be a good girl.'

I was hardly likely to wreck the house, was I? In the peace that followed, fresh memories came.

It was my first time in a car and every time I tried to stand up, the motion of the vehicle made me fall back onto the seat. When the car stopped we hadn't yet reached our final destination. We were in a line behind many other vehicles and when we got to the front, my rescuers showed cards to a man. A barrier opened and Andy drove in. Despite being scared about what was to happen to me, I was naturally curious, so I looked out of the window when I could. We passed lots of buildings and I noticed people hurrying from one place to another, some of them dressed in the same clothes as Andy and Smudge. We drove past more buildings that looked alike and had small green areas outside, some with flowers and some small stones. There were cars outside some of these and I noticed toys too. On we went, past these buildings where the area became greener. There were still grey structures but there was more space between each one. As Andy slowed the vehicle I heard barking. He stopped and lifted me out of the car.

'Welcome home, pal,' he said. He walked past more cars, towards a long, one-storey structure. Unlike the others we had passed, its roof was domed and made from a different material. It was long and wasn't as tall as the others. There were grassed areas outside and I could see behind it to the countryside. Smudge held open the door as we walked in. A number of people were sitting on comfortable looking chairs in one area, drinking out of mugs and eating. They were laughing and joking but stopped when they saw us. Seeing people eating made me realise how hungry I was and my stomach rumbled.

'Oh, the poor thing.' The words came from one of the two women in the group. She was the only person not dressed in the strange looking pyjamas that had now become a familiar sight.

'We found her on the beach,' said Smudge. 'I'll let Andy tell you what happened.'

Smudge put down a bowl and gave me food as Andy told the story. They all laughed at the bit about the dolphin and teased him good-naturedly. I tuned out after a while, too busy chomping my food down. I hadn't realised quite how hungry I was. I ate a bit too much and felt myself nodding off. I tried to fight it as they were now discussing my future, but I lost and went into a food coma.

I'm not sure how much later it was when I awoke. It was still light but there were less people there. I felt something around my neck and scratched it. It was new and strange but didn't hurt so I wasn't really worried. I'd only been shown kindness so far, and these people were a friendly bunch. Deep down, I knew they wouldn't hurt me. The woman in plain clothes stroked me, then put me in front of a bowl filled with water. As I drank thirstily, she went to a desk and picked up a phone. I could hear her speaking to someone but wasn't close enough to hear what was being said.

A woman dressed in the strange pyjamas arrived a few minutes later, together with Andy and Smudge. She spoke matter of factly as she picked me up and checked me over. I liked it here so far, so hoped I would pass her inspection.

'Can we keep her, boss?' Andy asked the woman, who spent a few seconds thinking about it.

'She's a Labrador crossed with a bit of Collie and Husky I think, so she could have some sort of retriever role and will probably be intelligent. She seems friendly enough.' The boss was talking almost to herself. 'Let's get the vet to check her over then do some simple tasks with her. Even though she's a puppy we should get an idea of what we can expect.'

'Shall I put her in with Digger,' Andy asked.

'Good idea.'

So I was poked and prodded some more by one of the people in white coats, and had every orifice looked into. Even worse, this time I had two thin sharp devices shoved into me and they hurt like crazy. I was later to discover these were called needles and would try to avoid them like the plague. They also took some blood from me and started calling me Fish. I was given a clean bill of health and heard the white coat man telling the boss that I was bright. She smiled, which told me it was a good thing to be. Although older now, I was still considered a puppy and I was quite exhausted by this stage, but I couldn't get any sleep just yet. They put me in a pen along with a dog who looked a similar age to me. He was sleeping so I looked longingly at what was to be my new bed, and approached it to sniff and ensure all was well. I heard a series of weird barks, as if he added ee, to the end of some. Digger had woken up and left his bed. He sidled up to the wall trying to make himself smaller and lower than I was. It was classic submissive behaviour and I wondered why he seemed frightened of me. I wandered over and we sniffed each other. With each sniff his attitude changed, then all hell broke loose as he went from submissive to something akin to a massive force of nature.

I ran around a bit with Digger who barked constantly. Although barks were individual, his was very unusual and I'd never heard anything like it.

'Don't shout, I'm not deaf,' I said, but he chose to ignore me, constantly asking questions but not waiting for the answers.

'Who are you? Where are you from? Why are you hereee?' Each question ended with the ee sound and it took me a while to get used to.

I gave up and stopped barking. I've never been one to make noise simply for the sake of it. Digger ran around for a bit, bent towards me, play bit me and wagged his tail. All this while telling me to join in his game. Despite being tired, he was such good fun that I couldn't resist. Our carers watched as we got to know each other.

'They're going to get on well,' said Andy. 'That'll please the boss.'

'Maybe Fish can calm him down a bit.'

I heard Smudge's comment and realised what they wanted me to do. So I ran around a bit more then barked at Digger to tell him I'd had enough and needed a rest. After a little protest I showed him I wasn't playing any more, then headed for my bed. Digger followed me and lay down beside me. It was a tight squeeze but I didn't mind. It had been a while since I'd felt the warmth of another dog next to me and I was reminded of my siblings, which made me feel sad, but the warmth also made me feel safe and secure. Digger was already asleep. Before I nodded off I saw Andy and Smudge high five each other, looking very pleased with themselves.

It felt like I'd been sleeping for ages and I wasn't yet ready to open my eyes when I heard the clang of metal on metal, then Digger chomping at some biscuits. Food was a good incentive, so I got up and ambled over to the bowl that Digger wasn't eating out of.

'Is this mine?' I asked. He looked at me, acknowledging the question but didn't answer. He was eating as if he hadn't been fed for weeks. As I'd been fed and watered quite generously since arrival, I wondered why he was so eager. With such dubious table manners, perhaps I ought to get stuck in and not give him the chance to wolf down my food as well.

The biscuits tasted much better than they looked. I was halfway through when, as suspected, Digger decided to chance his luck.

'You've finished yours,' I barked, gently at first. 'This is my breakfast.'

'I'm still hungreee,' he said as he nudged his head into my bowl.

I didn't want to argue with my kennel mate, but at the same time, I was no pushover. 'Get off my food, Digger, I'll not tell you again.'

He gave me a yeah-right look, then proceeded to eat my biscuits. I was nervous but knew I had to make a stand so I nipped him, just a little warning bite. He yelped and jumped backwards, but I couldn't believe it when he came back and stole another biscuit. This time I gave him a proper bite, followed up with a low growl, 'You greedy, selfish dog!'

That did the trick. He looked guilty as he moved towards his bed and I finished my food in peace. After breakfast, the guys got ready to take us out and I approached Digger. He wagged his tail, glad to see me, but acting as if nothing had happened.

'Don't do that again,' I said.

He had the decency to look sheepish. 'I'll do my best,' he said. 'If you knew how hard it was you might understand...'

'Right you two,' Andy interrupted any further conversation. 'Time for work, let's go.'

We would come to know that as the signal for our training to begin. I hoped Digger would tell me more later, but there was no time to dwell on it as we were tooled up in our leads and harnesses and led out of the pen. As we made our way to the training area, Andy and Smudge chatted about us. Apparently Digger liked to dig at everything but they weren't sure why. They also said we were quite young so didn't expect too much from us and planned on making it fun so they could keep our interest. Fun sounded good to me.

'We need to show them we're worth saving, Digger. Please give it your best shot.'

'I'll try, Fish,' he said, 'but paying attention isn't easy for meee.' As if to prove a point, he tried to run in front of me, but Andy tugged his lead, pulling him back.

At the training area, the first command we had to muster was to sit down. Simple, you might think, but not so easy when you're out in a field with your roomie who just wants to run around barking and digging holes. I thought if I tried hard, Digger might follow suit. When I got the hang of the sit and stay commands, he copied me and that's how the day went. I would be vain to think that Digger did it because of me. As soon as he saw that treats were involved, his concentration and interest increased substantially. After we had learnt how to do that, we were let off our leads for a while and allowed to run around. Then, harnesses back on, we were taught the next command. I was tired by the end of the session but I could sit and stay, shake hands with each of my front paws and also lie down on command. It took an average of three repetitions for me to catch on to what they wanted, but it was five for Digger who was not quite at my level of expertise. Whenever he'd had enough he showed the trainers by stopping what he was supposed to be doing and digging a hole. It seemed strange to me and I wondered what made him do it.

He decided to tell me before we went to sleep.

He didn't steal any of my biscuits that evening after wolfing down his own, but I could tell it was an effort. I dragged my bowl to the other side of the pen to eat, as far away from Digger as I could. When we'd finished, we were taken for a short walk so we could do our business, then closed in for the night. Both of us felt sleepy after our first day of training. Digger curled up in his own bed, and as the sun went down and I laid my head on my front paws, he began to talk like he had to...

'I was taken away from my mother, brothers and sisters at a very young age,' he said, 'and told I was to be a

51

hunting dog. I was amongst others the same as me and we had little to eat. It was every dog for themselves. Every scrap we were thrown was fought over. Where we lived was guarded by crazies.'

I raised a questioning eyebrow.

'Big dogs who had been treated as badly as we had, but taught to be aggressive. They didn't care who they hurt except for the master who they obeyed without question,' he shuddered as if remembering something awful.

'What happened?'

'I saw a puppy younger than me who had managed to get out of the enclosure. Two of the crazies killed her.'

'For the love of Lassie! How awful.'

'Awful was an understatement! We lived in constant fear for our safety, in filthy conditions, always hungry and thirsty. Yet we were expected to work hard on hunts when we barely had the energy to put one paw in front of the other.'

'So couldn't you escape while you were out hunting?'

'I could have tried,' said Digger. 'But we were told that escapees were always caught and never lived to tell the tale. I still had the mental picture of the puppy being savaged by the crazies, and was too frightened.'

'What if you weren't made for hunting and underperformed?'

'Oh, Fish, to have your innocence! Eee!'

Now wasn't the time to explain my life hadn't been a bed of roses so far.

'Those that underperformed were shot for sport, so that wasn't an option. We were between the devil and the deep blue sea-ee.'

'I know all about that, literally.'

'Really?' he asked.

'That's for another night, Digger. So what happened? How come you lived to tell the tale?'

'I knew I couldn't live like that and had to escape. I was fiercely protective of my corner of the pen so dug and dug. Nobody was interested in what I was doing. One night I had done enough to take me outside the perimeter fence into a field. I ran, knowing my life depended on it, with the sound of one of the crazies ringing in my ears. He told me he would find me and kill meee.'

'How awful.'

Digger was shaking with the memory of his earlier life. I couldn't believe the contrast between those who loved us and the cruelty of those who wanted to control and seemingly punish us, just for being alive.

'I'm all right, Fish,' he said, before giving a big sigh. 'I need to tell this, it's good for meee... I kept running. I'm not sure for how long, but darkness came at least twice. Whenever exhaustion forced me to stop I dug, even when I had little energy. I collapsed when I couldn't take one more step. I woke with the light and found myself on a hilly-grassed area. I was woken by the sound of many people and thought my time was up. I dug some more, then collapsed, unable to move. But these people in the pyjama uniforms were different. One held my head while another gave me water

53

out of her own bottle. They took me somewhere safe and fed and watered me. More importantly, I was shown human kindness for the first time in my life. Sometimes I forget that I don't have to fight for my food any more - but I can't stop digging.'

I left my bed and got in with Digger. His body was trembling. The warmth of each other brought us both comfort and eventually he stilled, and passed out into a deep sleep.

Not for the first time, I looked up to the stars, wondering what the future held for me.

The training continued at full-pace. I was constantly told I was clever, with a remarkable sense of smell too, and Digger was complimented for being exceptionally fast and agile. We performed for our trainers and visitors alike. It wasn't that difficult and tasty treats were always a good incentive. We were the only two dogs without dedicated handlers, though Andy insisted on being involved in all aspects of our training. A few other dogs had come and gone but we were the elite, the only ones good enough to stay without actually being chosen for the job. You can't imagine how good that made a couple of formerly homeless hounds feel. Scraped from the bottom of the pile with all the odds against us, it looked like we had struck gold, and with lots of hard work, could make something of ourselves. I can't say that being a working pooch was something I'd aspired to as a puppy. In fact, I hadn't aspired to anything before being thrown over the side of the boat, but I enjoyed working and so far it came easily to me. Digger felt the same. Well, I thought he did until we both became more confident of our abilities and he decided to speak to me about how he really felt.

'It's not easy having this life, Fish, when others are stuck in the living hell I escaped from.'

'It can't be helped,' I told him. 'You were lucky to escape and were far too young and weak to help others. You could barely help yourself from what you've told me.'

'You're right, of course-ee,' he said. And I thought that was the end of it.

By this stage in our training we could do all the basic tricks that people seemed to find amusing, like sitting, staying, rolling over, just about anything they wanted that involved paws, twirling around and barking to order. This was the fun stuff, but we could also sniff out explosives and weapons, something they would use us for in future I presumed. I could also recognise emotion on people's faces. I knew if they were lying and had a secret code that Andy had taught me. When he was playing cards, if I rolled my left paw underneath me when lying down, instead of my right, he knew the opponent who had last spoken was bluffing. His mates told him how much his card skills had improved within the last couple of months, but we both knew it was my skills and not Andy's that won him the games. I didn't mind. He had saved me, taken a chance on me and taught me skills that could only enhance my life, and I would be forever grateful.

Andy tried to talk his boss into letting him be my dedicated handler. He wanted to take me back to his room at the end of the day and get me out of the kennel I shared with Digger. She was having none of it, saying that my future in the section was not guaranteed, and neither was Digger's; money was short, further cutbacks were coming and decisions had to be made. I tried not to think about it, but like they all said, I wasn't stupid so it did play on my mind at times. Although both Digger and I could do all the tasks or tricks requested of us, our skillsets differed. He didn't have the ability to read human emotions, but there again, I didn't have his speed and although I was agile, my skills in that department were nothing compared to my buddy's. I did wonder once or twice whether they would pick him or me if only one of us could stay. I decided that wherever my roomie went, I would go with him. I hoped he felt the same.

Then, on an unusually hot spring day, we met a Pug named Bunty who would change the course of our lives, and take the decision about our future out of the hands of the Dog Section, and most certainly out of our paws.

Chapter 5

A different smell woke me early that morning. As I opened my eyes and sniffed, I knew a new dog had arrived. Andy was talking to the boss as he walked towards our kennel.

'So what did the letter say exactly?'

'It was just a note with barely legible writing. It said her name's Bunty, that she's untrainable and is the most stubborn dog in the world. It was in an envelope, right next to where they dumped her outside the gate. The cruelty of some people never ceases to amaze me.'

Andy nodded his head sadly, in agreement with the boss. 'Sounds like a challenge though,' he said. Then to us, 'Come on you two, time for work.'

Digger jumped up all eager to go. 'Come on, Sandee. Show some enthusiasm.'

'Shush I'm trying to listen,' I gave a gentle bark and he did as I asked.

'But seriously, what are you going to do?' Andy asked. 'Keep her here or send her to the shelter down the hill?'

'You know I think all dogs can be trained, right?'

'Yup, me too,' Andy replied.

'Fancy giving it a shot?'

'Why not,' he laughed.

'Great, I'll bring her over.'

'What Oh, old chaps,' Bunty said when she joined us. We quickly introduced ourselves but didn't have the time to get to know each other properly before our harnesses were on and we started work. Digger and I were into the usual routine, but Bunty gave me a slight nod and a wink when the handlers weren't looking. I knew they'd have their hands full with her and be pulling their hair out by the end of the day.

Andy put Digger and Bunty to one side, and while they were getting to know each other, did some one-on-one training with me. I assumed we would all have one-on-one's that day. Later on, we watched as Andy tried to get the best out of Bunty. She seemed slow and disinterested and I could see he was starting to get frustrated.

'Break time,' he shouted and the handlers went off for a coffee (and to discuss new techniques to try on Bunty, I imagined). Once they were out of sight, she waddled over to the exact spot where Digger had buried a ball earlier, dug it up and brought it back. Digger woofed a laugh and I gave her a rare smile. I didn't like to smile too much in front of people because they then expected me to do it on demand and it became a little tedious.

'So you do know that I'm jolly clever and can do all the tricks they want don't you?' she asked.

We said we did and she continued.

'Right, here's the situation, chaps. I need volunteers to accompany me on a mission. It's going to be dangerous but if we succeed we can save many dogs from a miserable and painful life.'

'And if we don't?' I asked.

'I'll be honest with you, old girl,' said Bunty. 'If we don't succeed, we could very well lose our lives at worst, or our freedom at best. Are you in?'

'I'm inee,' Digger was too eager in his reply and I smelled a rat. Looking from one to the other, I wondered what they knew that I didn't.

'Fish?'

'Considering everything Digger has been through, Bunty, he's rather eager to risk his life yet again. Isn't he?'

'My, you are as clever as the handlers say,' she said, and I felt a swell of pride. 'Digger told me all about his escape from that farm and those beastly animals. As it happens I'd already heard about the despicable cruelty there and have carried out some research.'

'That's a bit of a coincidence isn't it?'

'I make it my role in life to help others where I can. Now are you in or out?'

I ignored her question. 'So this mission is to save the dogs at the farm where Digger used to live? The farm where he saw those mad dogs murder a puppy?'

'Spot on, Fish, old girl. But we'll carry out at least one recce and I'll formulate a plan to ensure we have the best chance we can. I'm not going to lie to either of you,' she tapped a front paw on the ground, to emphasise her words, I thought. 'This is most serious and be absolutely clear that you could lose your freedom or your lives. Knowing what we do, I don't see how we can possibly continue to work here, and not do anything to help those less fortunate.'

Although I was keen to help, especially after such a rousing speech by Bunty, I was still terrified of the possible consequences. Bunty didn't need an answer right away so I said I'd sleep on it and we could discuss it again the following day.

'I'm in,' said Digger, 'whether you are or not, Fishee.'

'My chum Parky will join us too,' said Bunty, 'and, Fish, whatever you decide, the mission will still go ahead and nobody will think any worse of you.'

I looked at Digger and Bunty. Yeah, right, I thought, of course they wouldn't.

It took a while to get to sleep that night. As much as the sensible side of my brain told me to leave well alone, I already knew deep down that I would join the others, even if it was a suicide mission. I had no idea how we would break into the farm, arrange the escape of the captive dogs and get out of there without either coming to any harm, or being murdered by the crazy dogs who, according to Digger, seemed to enjoy being savages.

I was distracted the following day and faltered in my training, which had gone like a dream so far. Andy was patient to start with.

'What's the matter, girl?' he asked. 'Are you sickening for something?'

I gave him my best sad eyes look, which was rewarded with a cuddle.

'You're too soft with that dog.' Andy hadn't seen the boss. I'd sniffed her presence but was too busy enjoying my cuddle. With his arms around my head he whispered in my ear.

'Come on, Fish, let's show her. Do this for me please?'

I concentrated, deciding to double my efforts and not to let him down.

'I don't think so, boss,' he said. 'Watch this.'

He showed me a pistol and told me to sniff it. I obliged.

'Will you remember that smell, Fish?'

Of course I would. Did he think I was stupid or something?

'Would you like to hide it, boss?'

Andy sounded very confident and the boss said she would.

'Follow my Land Rover,' she said. 'I'll just get the keys.'

'No need,' Andy smiled. 'Fish, go get the keys.'

I went to the hooks he'd shown me in the reception area and collected the keys for the Land Rover. Returning outside I was unsure whether to give them to Andy or the boss. He had his arms folded and nodded towards her so I dropped them at her feet and wagged my tail. She laughed and gave me a pat, then I returned to Andy for my treat. He already had the keys to his Rover, so I jumped in the back as instructed and we followed the boss's Land Rover out into the countryside. When she stopped the vehicle she told Andy to wait until she returned. He played with his phone while I sniffed the area. I could smell the pistol, even though the boss had masked it with her own scent. We made a start when she came back. I was enjoying myself and had been

61

able to put the worry about the possible mission on the back burner. I redeemed myself by finding the pistol. The boss had buried it behind a pungent bush, in the hope I would be put off by the plant, no doubt.

'Well?' asked Andy.

'Well indeed. That was pretty amazing,' she said, before bending to give me lots of cuddles. This was quite rare for her. She didn't speak to me but addressed Andy.

'You want to watch this one, she's a bit too clever for her boots.'

'She's fine, aren't you, Fish?' Now he joined in the cuddle fest and I loved the attention. 'She loves being with us. Perhaps now you'll think about making me her permanent handler?'

'Ah,' said the boss. 'That's not going to happen, Andy.'

He gave a questioning look and, as I walked by his side back toward the vehicles, I listened to their conversation.

'I received notification yesterday that they need a Dog Handler in Afghan.'

'But I have another year here, and did a tour before this posting...'

'I know,' she cut him off. 'But Major Finn asked for you specifically. I fought your corner, Andy, but it's on promotion. Welcome to the Sergeants' Mess.'

She leaned over and shook his hand. I could sense he wasn't happy, even though the boss made promotion sound like good news.

'Cheers,' he said. 'But I'd still rather stay here.' He stopped walking and bent down to me, giving me a stroke and telling me how clever I was.

'You're too attached to that dog,' she told him. 'You know the rules, and it will be good for you to get away from her.'

'You just don't get it, do you?' He didn't wait for an answer as he said, 'Come on, Fish,' then jogged away, before picking up speed. I followed, easily keeping up with him though he ran as if being chased by a pack of crazies.

I would soon know that feeling.

I heard Ben yawning as he walked down the stairs. I must have been deep in thought as I usually heard either of them before they opened the bedroom door. I rushed to get to the bottom of the stairs before he did. He was dressed in casual clothes and training shoes. Great, he was taking me out.

'We'll go for a walk, then when Ellie comes home I'll do some housework to get back in her good books.'

'Good idea, Ben. But never mind the housework, let's get out there.'

'Shall I have a cup of tea first?'

'Err, no,' I headed for the box in the utility room where they kept my lead and some of my toys. I put my front paws up and grabbed the lead in my mouth. Wagging my tail, I took the lead into the living room and placed it in front of Ben. He was suitably impressed.

'Who's a clever girl then, Sandy?'

He praised me again, put the lead on, and off we went. Training could work both ways and I was happy with the way my people parents were progressing, so far.

About halfway into our usual route Ben said hi to a woman he called Nicole, who I hadn't met before. Seeing my wagging tail, she bent down to give me a friendly pat. I reciprocated with a head nudge that made most women fall for me.

'Oh how, sweet,' she said. 'Isn't she lov...'

Her words were cut off by barking and growling as a dog bounded over to me to have a go. Nicole grabbed him but he was still shouting.

'Leaveheralone, Fish. She'sminenotyours. Go on, getawayfromher,' he said, and I was surprised that the one hundred mile an hour speech and such a high-pitched anxious-sounding bark, could come from a fairly large Collie cross.

'Behave yourself, Chip,' Nicole scolded and he calmed down.

More like Psycho, than Chip, I thought as I watched him spin around in small circles, barking like a maniac as he did so.

'Ithought youweredead,' he said. 'Wealldid.'

Totally bamboozled, I looked at him, trying to recall where we had met. I had a flashback of a tall, chunky dog snapping and snarling at me, and it felt so real I howled, then peed on the spot.

'You've frightened her, you naughty boy,' Nicole said to Chip. He had the grace to look guilty and did calm down a little, though he knew full well that he wasn't the cause of my fear.

'I'm sorry, but I don't remember you. I've lost my memory. Some of my memories are coming back and I'm trying to piece them together. I don't mean to be rude either, but I have my own people parents and have no intention of trying to steal yours, or anyone else's for that matter.'

'Thankyou forsaving mylife,' he said.

Another flashback where Chip was cowering in the corner of a farm shed. I attempted to coax him out but he lay there, trembling. I had tried to be nice but had to be tough with him to force him to leave. '*Aden, if you want to live, get into the tunnel and run like you've never run before.*'

'Aden,' I said, 'your other name was Aden.'

'It'sbeen awhile,' he screeched.

I walked as far as my extendable lead and Ben would allow. My people parents had been told not to let me off the lead on walks for the first two months, in case I absconded. That wasn't going to happen but they weren't to know.

Away from the humans, we talked. Chip was even more messed up than Digger, no Obie, I corrected myself. When I asked for more details about how we met he got all grizzly again. Nicole shouted at him and he rushed to her side, eager to please, then did a couple of spins just for the sake of it as far as I could see. I wondered if he would ever get over the past. I also wondered if I wanted my memories to return, knowing how the experience had affected the other dogs. The only one who seemed relatively sane was Lola, but I didn't know the extent of her involvement in the mission.

Something had gone drastically wrong to leave the other two like this and to give me amnesia.

Ben was talking to Nicole and I cocked an ear to listen.

'They seem to be getting along much better now. Ellie will be chuffed. We're not sure how many other dogs Sandy was in contact with before the rescue centre, so want to socialise her. Ellie will probably contact you to arrange a play date sometime next week.'

Nicole said that would be great, then we said goodbye and made our way home. Ellie had already unpacked the shopping, and after our reunion she gave me a marrowbone filled with yummy meat. I sat outside on the pretend grass, contentedly sucking and chewing. The sun was shining, my humans were happy, and the swallows were dive-bombing the pool. Life was good.

Swallows. A distant memory stirred. I didn't want it so tried to make it go away but it downright refused. Putting the bone to one side I closed my eyes, waiting for the inevitable.

I was back in the section with Digger and Bunty.

'We need to work out how to distract those beastly crazies, while others get into the facility to release the captives,' Bunty said.

'Are you serious?' I worried for her sanity having heard Digger's story.

'Never more so. We can't sit by and do nothing while those poor animals suffer in silence. I know what

66

Digger endured and have no doubt other dogs are going through the same, and worse.'

Details of her discussions with Digger were slowly unravelling and I looked at them both, wondering what else had taken place out of my earshot. Digger didn't catch on, but Bunty did.

'I know the layout of the facility, where the crazies live and eat and the routines of the humans. Night-time is the quietest, especially if they're going to do an all-night hunt this year, like they did last. That would be the absolute best time to go in, so we can be there to rescue the captive dogs as soon as they return, while the crazies are tired and distracted.'

I looked at her, knowing that pugs weren't bred for agility or speed. She might be cunning, but there was no way she could out run the crazies. It didn't occur to me not to help. I was terrified of the possible outcome, but even more frightened for the safety of my friend Digger, and for the lives of the poor souls stuck in there. Remembering my mistress from the boat, I knew what cruelty was, so I had to stand up to the mark, whatever the consequences. There was also another reason. I'd grown attached to Andy and now that he was leaving, the section wasn't as important to me.

We recce'd the farm from a distance. There was an outer perimeter fence with warning signs posted at regular intervals. Even if they didn't read the signs, humans would have no doubt about the dogs inside. The noise was deafening. Two of the crazies were on long chains and walked the length of them, pulling and jumping, testing the strength of the chains at regular intervals, and their own ability to break them. There were holes in the fence we could get through, but that wasn't the point of the recce. After watching the chained dogs, we knew their range so would be able to stay out of their reach. There wasn't much noise from the captive dogs.

Chapter 6

A few days later, Bunty informed us that the mission was to take place that night, while the hunters and their dogs were out on the annual night hunt.

'How do you know that?'

She looked at me as if I were stupid and tapped a front paw. 'Fish old girl, as I've told you before, I use Social Media. You can find out anything on Facebook if you're clever enough.'

She expected me to believe that she could use the computer; a machine that all humans I knew were obsessed with. I knew she was clever, but...

'Anyway, that's not important, the mission is, so stay focussed while I remind you all of the plan.'

It was the fourth or fifth time we'd been told what was to happen. It was deeply ingrained in the hope that it would become second nature to us. After leaving the section, we were to remove each other's collars with our teeth, so there would be no repercussions for our human caretakers if any of us were caught. We'd arrive as soon as darkness fell. Digger would carry on with the hole he had already started at the back of the farm, leading to the shed where the hunting dogs were kept, and start to release the captives. Me and Parky were to run along the front of the fence, keeping the crazies occupied while Digger was busy, and I was to enlarge the hole already in the front of the fence, so we could use that if it all went wrong.

The second back-up involved Bunty placing pre-poisoned meat for the crazies to eat in their guard area, hopefully killing them all. Then Parky and me were to make our way around the back when the hunting party returned, go into Digger's tunnel, and bring any remaining dogs out one by one, as quietly as we could. While we were doing this, Digger would make another hole and put some strong-smelling meat in there, also poisonous. If anyone was chased down the hole, the idea was the crazies would go for the food, rather than chasing one of the hunting dogs and us.

As I often heard Smudge say to Andy, 'no plan survives first contact,' and Bunty was perfectly aware of this, hence the back-up hole in the front fence, the poisoned meat and the poisonous food in the hole. I thought the first two were good ideas but was sceptical about the third. I couldn't envisage any mad dogs stopping a chase to eat, and then resuming. Digger believed the crazies weren't fed enough so thought it worth a try. We were as ready to go as we could ever be.

Bunty made Digger cover himself in the orange clay that was plentiful in the countryside around the section, and I took the mickey out of his appearance. It was a fab disguise and I wouldn't have recognised him if I hadn't already known it was him. And his scent was different. I was renowned in our small dog world for being able to sniff out anything, but even I couldn't recognise Digger. The clay had done an excellent job of masking him so I knew the crazies wouldn't recognise his smell either. It gave me a little confidence but I was still hyped-up and felt the adrenaline pulsing through my body.

Bunty checked us before we left. We were tooled up but only carrying the bare essentials. One of these was a poison pill. If it all went wrong and we had the opportunity, we could swallow the pill rather than suffer the pain that would be inflicted by the crazies – a sobering thought indeed.

As instructed, we waited an hour then checked on Digger. He had re-opened the tunnel through which he'd escaped and said there was enough room for the biggest captive to get through with ease. Bunty took him to where she'd hidden the poisoned meat. Digger unwrapped a chunk with his mouth and paws, being careful to avoid the area where Bunty had put the poison. It was rank but would make most dogs follow the scent if they got a sniff of it. Digger put it in his mouth without another thought and headed back to the second hole.

Parky and I made our move to the front of the fence. As Bunty had predicted, there were only two crazies there and they were both chained. We ran along our side of the fence to get their attention. They followed on the inside, growling threateningly and barking as they did so. We stopped at the limit of their chains.

Both crazies were male and Parky addressed the bigger of the two. 'I thought you were a bitch,' he said. 'Call that scary? You wouldn't even frighten a kitten.'

The dog went ballistic, head butting the fence while barking at Parky that he was going to catch him and make him suffer. It was frightening to watch. We knew the fence

71

would hold, even though it shuddered with every attack from the crazy big dog. They seemed too stupid to realise this was a diversion and Bunty was able to get through the hole in the fence, place the meat in the area we'd first seen them, and get out before we all turned at the sight of vehicle headlights, indicating the return of the hunting parties. The sun wasn't yet fully up so the lights were still needed in the countryside.

That's when it all started to go wrong.

Both of the crazies on the chains had eaten the meat. The smaller was starting to lose consciousness and would no longer be useful, not so the dog that had threatened Parky. He barked, shouting to his returning pack on the truck.

'We've been poisoned. Trespassers. One blonde bitch, one black dog with curly fur. Make them pay for what they've done. Kill them for us...'

His bark petered out but he'd said enough to alert the others and to cause mayhem.

We ran around the back as quickly as our legs would allow. The hunters shouted at the crazies, telling them to shepherd the other dogs into their shed. One of the crazies barked, trying to alert them to our presence. He was rewarded with a whack from the stick the man carried, so changed his mind, deciding to carry out the order. The hunters locked up the guard dogs. Keen to get stuck into their boozy breakfast, they didn't chain the dogs as Bunty had expected. We ran to the back to help Digger, and soon noticed dogs running for their lives through the countryside. As instructed, Digger had briefed them to run until they came to an urban area, where the chance of being picked up

72

and taken to one of the many rescue centres on the island was better than in the countryside.

I dragged out the last but one dog. He thanked me then loped off. Parky seemed to be taking his time so I was in two minds what to do for the best. Slower than the rest of us, Bunty had already left, but Digger was waiting and becoming impatient.

'Come on, Fish. We need to get out of here before they find us-ee.'

I knew what we had to do but Parky was still in there. What if something had happened to him?

'I can't leave him, Digger. Or the one dog that's left. I'm going in.'

'I'll come with you,' he replied.

'The tunnel's not big enough for all of us,' I said. 'You make your way back and I'll see you there.'

I headed back through the tunnel. Though I already knew that something had gone wrong, I wasn't prepared for the sight that met my eyes.

Parky was in the corner, his body limp, lifeless and covered in blood. The crazy who had done this lifted his head and growled. I looked into his eyes. There was no remorse, only madness. I felt like a rabbit caught in the headlights. Trembling with fear, I couldn't take my eyes off the gruesome sight in front of me. Parky had been brave and loveable; he didn't deserve that, nobody did. The red mist came down and I wanted to destroy the crazy. I remembered listening to Andy and Smudge discussing military tactics and also lack of control in humans. They reckoned controlled

73

aggression was needed in any fight or battle. I was unsure whether that would work here, but then I heard whimpering. I dragged my eyes away from the horrific scene in front of me, looking to the direction of the sound.

He was a Collie cross and looked about my age.

'We'regoing todie,' he said, talking at the speed of light but quite matter of factly under the circumstances, though in a very high-pitched tone that didn't match his size, 'andit'sgoingto bepainful.'

'What's your name?'

'Aden.'

'Aden,' I leaned over to him and whispered so the crazy couldn't hear. 'If you want to live, get into the tunnel,' I pointed with my nose, 'and run like you've never run before. My mate Digger is just in front of us. Follow the scent of clay when you come out of the tunnel and you'll find him.'

'ButIcan't, whatif...'

'Go on, son,' I said, 'you can do it.'

'I'mnot...'

'You have a choice, Aden. Another chance at life or you die here. Now go!' It did the trick and he scurried down the hole.

I leapt at the crazy and landed by his leg. I took a big chunk out of his calf and the savage looked startled as he let out a scream. He got up and swiped me, the strength of the hit knocking me into the wall. I was mad and upset about Parky so I jumped at him again. I was sure at that stage I was going to die so, forgetting about the pill, was determined to go down fighting. He went to bite me but I managed to dodge, avoiding his teeth. I heard a commotion in the distance. Knowing other crazies would join us shortly, the red mist started to lift and self-preservation kicked in. I followed Aden into the hole and ran as if being chased by the hounds of hell.

I soon was.

There was no sign of Aden when I left the tunnel. Seeing Digger had waited instead of going on ahead, I shouted for him to run.

'I'm not leaving without you-ee,' he said, but then I saw the terror in his eyes and knew the crazies were behind me. 'Go,' I shouted and this time he went. Neither of us knew that the next time we met, I would struggle to remember him.

Always faster than me, it wasn't long before Digger had disappeared into the treeline. If the crazies concentrated on me, Digger and Aden would be safe.

Soon I was surrounded by four of them and they circled slowly, seemingly confident that I couldn't escape. I heard shouting and laughter, then saw two people approaching us. Great, I was going to be saved.

I should have known better given the state of the hunting dogs and their homes.

One shouted. 'Get her, Henry, show us what you can do.'

'For the love of Lassie,' I thought as Henry slowly approached me, his mouth dripping saliva, and blood lust in his eyes. He certainly doesn't look like a Henry, was my inappropriate thought as he leaped at me. Regaining my focus I jumped to the side as quickly as I could. The man who hadn't spoken laughed and the other punched him, which caused the crazies to look at them both, giving me the diversion I needed.

It was only a few seconds, but it gave me enough time to act; I ran under the legs of the biggest dog and sprinted for my very life. I had no idea where I was heading but ran, and ran. They followed, barking and growling as they did so.

The last thing I heard was one shouting, 'You'll never be safe, Blondie. I will hunt you down, mongrel, and kill you.'

Concentrating on the threat, I hardly noticed the insult that went with it. Like a dog possessed, I kept running and running. The sun reached its zenith, then later, dipped over the horizon and still I ran. When my legs couldn't take another step, I collapsed, exhausted, in a heap. The sound of distant barking brought me out of my deepest ever sleep.

'We're coming to get you, Blondie. You're going to die.' It was said in a conversational tone, but sent shivers down my spine. Still exhausted, hungry and thirsty beyond measure, my legs moved of their own accord and I ran as fast as I could, wondering how much more I had in me.

It was starting to get dark again as I came out of the countryside onto a road and kept on running. Bright lights blinded me so I couldn't see anything behind them. The car hit my side as I was almost halfway across the road.

The last thing I remember was flying through the air. The adrenaline was pumping through my body so at least there was no pain. For the second time in two days I thought I was going to die. I landed, hitting my head as I did so, and there was nothing but sweet oblivion.

I don't know how long I was out of it but when I came round I was buried under a bed of dirt and leaves in a forest. I had no idea who I was, where I came from or why I was there. I dug my way out and checked myself over. My ribs were almost sticking out of my sides and I was skin and bone. My mouth was so dry that my tongue stuck to the roof and I had to pull it off. I felt weak and had to drag myself to get moving, knowing if I lay down again, I wouldn't get up. I walked unsteadily. Eventually I came out of the forest onto a roadside. A car sped past making me cower and shake. I forced myself onward, hoping to find something to eat or drink soon; I didn't have much left in me. Other traffic passed. I jumped at the sound of a horn and decided my best bet was to return to the forest and lie down. As I made this decision, a vehicle stopped, just ahead of me.

I didn't have the energy to run away so stood still, and that's how Shel found me.

As soon as Ben and Ellie left for work, Bunty came over as promised.

'Do I know everything now?' I asked.

'Almost, Sandy.'

So there was something else and why was she calling me Sandy? She must have known the questions were on the tip of my tongue.

'I have special skills, old girl; so do you and Obie. Chip has bags of enthusiasm and natural talent, so he's one of us too. There are so many injustices and I believe we're all here to help those less gifted and not as fortunate as our good selves.'

'Cut to the chase, Bunty, my ego doesn't need massaging.'

'Sandy!' The look she gave made me feel as if I'd pooped on the rug. 'I wouldn't dream of massaging your ego. I simply want you to be aware of your own abilities, and to use them to help others. Are you in or out?'

'Depends what it involves, and why are you calling me Sandy now?'

'It involves whatever comes up at the time. We've survived the crazies but I can't promise we won't face other dangers. It's better if we only use our code names when we're on missions, we're regular dogs at all other times, keeping our people parents happy and training them as and when necessary,' she tapped her front left paw a few times, 'Are you in or out?'

I enjoyed a good life with my forever family and was blessed with lots of four-legged friends, but I was highly trained and did sometimes get bored in the house on my own. Perhaps it was possible to have the best of both worlds; a great family life but work undercover with Lola, AKA Bunty, and the others, as and when needed. I remembered Andy always telling me to finish the job. The job of fighting injustice would never be finished. Weaker or less fortunate animals needed dogs like us to improve their lives like ours had been improved.

'I'm in,' I said.

'Whatever it takes?' she asked.

'Yes. I hope I'm not going to regret this.'

'Jolly good.' Lola gave me her strange Puggy smile and lifted a paw. We high-fived and she left shortly after, saying that Gina was home early that day and had arranged pamper sessions for them both.

'All in the line of duty, old girl,' she said.

I laughed. My four-legged boss could be proper girly at times.

I nodded off shortly after, wondering what new adventures and dangers I had signed up for.

The rest of the morning passed in the usual round of sleep, playing with my toys and listening to the radio. An unexpected storm had blown in and it was tipping down with rain. I decided not to unlock the door and go outside, knowing I wouldn't be able to hide my unique wet dog smell from Ben and Ellie later. The intruder cat had got caught in the storm though, so I gave a soft chuckle bark as it ran past, then waved my paw and looked smugly at it. It stopped to have a go at me through the window, then realised it would get even wetter, so scurried away. I had no doubt it was planning something nasty for me in future.

Ellie arrived home first, then wished she hadn't when I took her my lead after she'd fussed over me for an appropriate amount of time. She put her soaking umbrella in the sink in the utility room and tried some blackmail.

'Ooh, look, Sandy. A lovely treat for you,' she said before giving me a gravy flavoured bone-shaped biscuit. I really wanted to get out but it would have been churlish to refuse her kind gesture, so I accepted the treat.

'Good girl,' she tickled me behind an ear. 'Daddy will be home shortly, then he'll take you out.'

I don't think so Ellie. I went to the patio door and looked out. She didn't take the hint so then I went to the front door, back to Ellie, then back to the door.

'Oh no, Sandy. Can't you wait until daddy comes home?'

She really didn't like the rain so was refusing to see the obvious. Sometimes I had to be extremely patient with my people parents. I approached the door again, turned around and gave Ellie an apologetic look. Then I squatted. She jumped off the settee quicker than you could say Lassie come home.

'No, Sandy, don't! It's okay.' She opened the door for me and I waited outside under cover while she quickly changed into sports trousers and grabbed her hooded jacket. Off we went and I forced myself to pee outside the gate, just to show that I had needed to go.

I didn't mind walking in the rain but it wasn't Ellie's favourite pastime, so she cut the walk short. Ben's car was there when we returned, and so was another vehicle, one I hadn't seen before.

My heart raced as I recognised his scent as soon as we neared the house. Why was he here and what did he want? But most importantly, how had he found me. What if he wanted me? And what did I want? My head was buzzing and I forced myself to calm down by following a deep-breathing technique I'd learnt from sneakily watching the handlers, back in my days at the section.

Ben called to Ellie that we had a visitor. Now calm, I decided to be myself, otherwise my people parents might suspect something untoward. I followed Ellie through to the lounge and headed for Ben. He gave me big loves, even more so than usual; it was as if he was trying to prove something. A sucker for cuddles, I reciprocated.

'Come and say hello, Fish,' said Andy.

It took all my willpower not to turn as he called what was now my code name.

'See, she doesn't know you,' said Ben, and Ellie asked what was going on.

As Ben explained, I ambled over to Andy and allowed him to stroke me, not showing him any more affection than I would a regular visitor. It was the first time I'd seen him out of uniform or overalls. He looked tired, a bit thinner, and his left foot and lower leg had been replaced by a false one, but he seemed fine.

'I would know this dog anywhere,' he said. 'This is definitely Fish. She's a highly trained military dog and has talents that I've never seen, not even in the best dogs I've trained and worked with. We think she unlocked her pen so she could escape with another dog.'

Ellie laughed, then tried to turn it into a cough when she saw the look on Andy's face.

'Are you from the military base on the island?' asked Ben.

'I was for a bit then spent some time in Afghan, then the UK getting used to this,' he said, nodding towards his left foot.

'Sorry about...' said Ellie.

'Thanks. I'm used to it now and luckier than...' Andy closed his eyes for a few seconds and an awkward silence followed. I nudged his hand and he stroked me, returning to the present.

'The military base,' said Ben, changing the subject. 'That must be what, two hundred miles away from the rescue centre where we found Sandy?'

'More like three hundred,' said Andy, 'but dogs have been known to walk long distances and anything's possible with Fish. She...'

'Look I'm really sorry..., for everything,' Ellie cut him off, 'but you're mistaken as far as Sandy's concerned. I know she's a rescue dog but she's a regular pet. Obviously she's very special to us, but she can't unlock doors, hasn't found any illegal drugs anywhere, can't sniff out bombs and as far as I know, her abilities are the same as other dogs of her breed.'

'I'm telling you that this is Fish. I know it's going to be difficult but I'd like you to think about giving her up, so we can continue her training and she can work as a military dog,' he sighed. 'My dog died in Afghanistan so I would be her handler which is what I wanted when we first took her in.'

'You can't do this,' said Ben, shaking his head before standing up. Andy stood up too and I could feel the tension in the room. I decided to stand by Ellie, but was ready to intervene if necessary.

'Why don't we let Sandy decide?'

Thanks a bunch guys, I thought, wondering what to do for the best.

The men stopped sizing each other up and looked at Ellie.

'I'm happy with that,' said Andy.

He seemed confident that I would return to him. Bit presumptuous I thought. I noticed Ben falter - so he believed Andy's story. That was an interesting development.

'Ben?' asked Ellie. He nodded, then they made their way outside. I followed without being asked.

'Sandy, come,' called Ellie.

'Here, Fish,' said Andy. 'We have a job to finish.'

I loved them all and had no doubt they felt the same. I was going to break the heart of my third favourite person in the world.

I trotted over to Ben and Ellie, wagging my tail so much it was doing the propeller thing again. Andy knew he was beaten and came over to us.

'I know it's you, Fish,' he said as he bent down to caress me. 'I'll always love you.'

It was unlike Andy to be so emotional and I was touched. He had no idea that Lola and Obie were in the village, so I hoped he didn't think I'd chosen the easy life. If I had gone back to him I'm not sure I could have dealt with the loneliness if he went away without me, or if something awful happened to him. He buried his head in my fur then gave me a final cuddle before whispering in my ear, 'Come and find me if you change your mind...'

Sorry, Andy, it's not going to happen. I licked his face before he stood up straight to address Ben and Ellie.

'I can see you love her and know she'll have a good life with you. Take care of her. Bye, Fish.'

They all shook hands.

'I'm sorry for your disappointment,' said Ellie, choosing her words carefully, I thought.

Andy walked down the drive, shoulders slumped and head down. I couldn't watch so turned away and walked into the house.

If only he knew I had resolved to live by his mantra, deciding to 'finish the job,' here on the island. Whatever and wherever that involved I would make him proud of me, even though our paths wouldn't cross again.

My eyes followed his every move as he got into his car, preparing to drive away. It was emotional watching him go, but I was strangely excited at the thought of my next adventure with the rest of my dog squad.

I didn't know then that it was the sort of excitement I could have done without.

Acknowledgements

Thanks to my husband Allan for listening (or doing a good job of pretending to listen), to my editor Jill Turner, to Jessica Bell for another fantastic cover, and to my friends Trudy Eitschberger, Julie Woodruff, Su Echo Falls S'ari, Charity Rowell and Rachel Crawford. Thanks also to all my other friends and readers for your support.

Author's Note

Thank you for purchasing this book. I hope you enjoyed reading it as much as I did writing it. Any reviews are gratefully received – I love reading them all.

Check out my website for my other books and special offers, or connect with me on Facebook at these links: https://debmcewansbooksandblogs.com
https://www.facebook.com/DebMcEwansbooksandblogs/?ref
=bookmarks

Printed in Great Britain
by Amazon